TILL THE
END OF TIME

Derek Sheffield
Rolvenden, 1995

Derek Sheffield is married and lives at Rovenden in Kent

TILL THE END OF TIME

A KENTISH CHRONICLE

Meresborough Books
17 Station Road, Rainham
Gillingham, Kent ME8 7RS
1995

Published for Derek Sheffield by
Meresborough Books
17 Station Road, Rainham
Gillingham, Kent ME8 7RS

Meresborough Books is a specialist publisher of books on Kent, with over
one hundred titles currently in print.
Their monthly magazine, *Bygone Kent*, was launched in 1979 and costs
£21 for an annual subscription
Full list of books available sent on request

First published 1995
© Copyright 1995, Derek Sheffield
ISBN 0948193824

Printed and bound in Great Britain by
Mackays of Chatham PLC, Chatham, Kent

CONTENTS

This books is dedicated to
The family who once lived in Yewtree House at Chelsfield in
the county of Kent

They are now resting peacefully in the churchyard of
St Martin of Tours

I think of them every day: I will never forget them
They gave me the happiest years of my life

and

Emily and Lucy Kelly
Two of the prettiest little girls I know

ACKNOWLEDGEMENTS

I am particularly grateful to the literary editors and reviewers of two local newspapers, for the coverage that they have given me on the first two books of this trilogy.

Clive Page of the Kentish Times Group of newspapers, for his kind reviews and constructive observations. I particularly appreciated his comment that he felt that my stories 'came from the heart', because that is exactly what they did. Clive Page, although younger than me, is of my time. He remembers things that I do, he understands the values that once existed. I was lucky indeed to have his support.

Deryn Eggington and Amanda Nash of the *News Shopper*, were also very kind to me. Their informative reviews, and the impressive centre-spread-displays that their newspaper gave me were very much appreciated.

Undoubtedly, the coverage given by these newspapers, resulted in the first of the trilogy selling 980 copies in the first two weeks of publication, and the second receiving orders for 1200 copies *on the first day*. Both of these books are now sold out. Reprints are due to be released on the same publication day, as the last of this trilogy.

I am most appreciative to Jane Austin and the staff of W H Smith & Co of Orpington, who have shown me great support. They commented that although these books could be said to have been of local interest, they could equally have applied to any village in the southern counties. They said that they stood on their own merit as being very good stories.

I must extend my very sincere thanks to Mr Quentin McCabe of Bentalls of Tonbridge. Mr McCabe has shown great confidence in this trilogy, which I know, has been reflected in its sales. I thank him for his support.

My thanks must go to Philip Lane, for access to his magnificent collection of antique photographs. These, together with some of my own photographs, provide the faces that go with the names, that are mentioned many times in the books.

Similar appreciation must be given to Mr Mark Gregson of Wordsworths of Orpington, and to all Post Offices and bookshops in the Weald of Kent. I owe them all a debt of gratitude, for bringing to the attention of the literary public, the story of Grannie, Grandad, and the family.

My appreciation is for promoting a series of chronicles dedicated to these wonderful folk. By bringing the story to ten thousand people throughout the country, who would not otherwise have known of the magic of these times. They have put on record a memorial that is cast in print, to Grannie and Grandad and the people of Maypole and Chelsfield that will live for ever.

No appreciation would be complete, without including the actual people involved in the production of this trilogy; Keith Grieve, Derek Harris, Linda Bustard, and the staff at Mackays of Chatham. Jumad Ganges for typesetting and the three cover designs. And last, but not least, Paul Butler of Meresborough Books of Gillingham for putting up with my constant worrying, in such a kindly manner.

LIST OF ILLUSTRATIONS

SECTION ONE

Facing page 64

SECTION TWO

Facing page 128

INTRODUCTION

I stated at the conclusion of my last book, that it was the end of a story, and would be the last book written on a way of life that ended with the passing of Grannie and Grandad, and the destruction of the old cottage where we had all lived happily for so many years.

I was completely and utterly wrong. A simple event can have many aspects when seen from different points of view; it can also have surprising consequences when viewed with the passage of time. So there is no such thing as an end to a story: purely a point at which the subject becomes exhausted and events begin to lose their interest.

The first of the three Chronicles *This Forgotten Place* dealt with the lives of Grandad, Grannie, their two daughters, Dorrie and Little Nell, with their respective sons Bryan and Derek. It also included Grandad's dreadful brother, Ern. The story was of their lives at *Yewtree House* in the hamlet of Maypole, and the parish of Chelsfield, in the county of Kent. The period covered, was from the origins of the family in a keepers' cottage in Shoreham Woods in the latter part of the 1890s; up to 1963.

The second of the trilogy, *And Then There Were None*, was broadened to include local people and the events of their time, in Chelsfield, Maypole, and Well Hill. It dealt in more detail with events concerning the 1939–45 war, and detailed the end of an era – the demise of Chelsfield village and its two hamlets.

The third and last of the trilogy came about because the two previous books have resulted in many of us from the old times coming together to talk of the past. The list at present is up to twenty. We meet for lunch at any of the four public houses that marked the boundary of our patch: The *Five Bells*, the *Bo-Peep*, the *Rock and Fountain*, and the *Kent Hounds*. These are not particularly gastronomic or alcoholic occasions, we try to organise food that would be of our time, at a price that can be afforded by all. It is simply an excuse to meet old friends and talk of old times. It is because I have been asked why I have omitted so many of these events, and because I have heard so many different conclusions to things that happened fifty years ago, that I have been prompted to complete this trilogy by writing *Till the End of Time*.

This story, therefore, is simply a humorous collection of all the things that I missed out. It is a tale of hot, balmy summers, with an abundance of wild flowers on the sides of narrow country lanes; of bitter, freezing winters, with frozen milk two inches tall standing out of milk bottles; of ice, thick on the inside of living-room windows. It was a time when old men with white beards stood with wheel-barrows in the middle of Chelsfield village, whilst the chickens scratched in the dust at the sides of the road. It is a story of soft, green grass, larks on high, and straw-chewing country boys.

I wrote at the conclusion of my last book, that it was the end of a story. Well this really is. Make the most of it; read and savour every word, because there is no more to come. When you are laughing at the tales of Grannie and Grandad, spare a thought for the unfortunate people of today who have never tasted Grannie's cooking, experienced the comfort of a deep, feather bed, or even known real friendship.

In the high-powered life they live; *they have forgotten how to live.*

Derek Sheffield, Rolvenden, 1995

CHAPTER ONE

A Tin of Paint

It was all Grannie's fault; If she had not diagnosed jaundice and dosed Ernie with a particularly potent dose of her jollop, it would never have happened.

Admittedly, Grannie said that because Ernie never complained again of feeling 'seedy', her mixture had worked; what she did not know, was that her cure was so cataclysmic, that he was too frightened to mention that he felt off-colour again! The absolute truth was that he sat groaning in the 'little house' up the garden for many hours; when he finally did appear, he sank on the garden seat in a state of shock and waited to die. It was Grandad who suggested that Ern's pallor was not normal, and that a visit from the doctor could well be in order.

Thus it was, that Doctor Grant was summoned from Orpington – on a mission of mercy – to deal with Grandad's brother, Ern, on a matter that was not mentionable.

The trouble came when the doctor decided to carry out an examination – there was no way that Ern would take his vest off; "'Ent never 'ad it orf before," he said "and 'ent a'takin' it orf now!" When an irate Doctor Grant insisted on the removal of the offending garment, Ern complained that he "would catch his death if he did."

Doctor Grant shouted that he "would bloody well die if he didn't!" It was all very fraught.

This all took place in the bedroom; it was because Ern was stone deaf and the doctor had to shout, that we heard everything with great clarity.

After examining the top half in detail, the doctor said "come along man, take your underpants off!"

Ern refused point blank. "I 'ent takin' 'em orf fer no one, least of all you!"

Doctor Grant cursed and fumed but all to no avail. He finally came downstairs, where we all pretended that we had not heard, and pronounced that he could find nothing wrong from the waist up, but suspected some form of food poisoning. The only way that he could verify that, he said, was to examine a stool of Ernies. He asked that we send this down to his surgery in Orpington within the next few days.

This caused a problem. Everyone stood with blank expressions; nobody knew what he was talking about. "Wot the 'ell's he want with brother Ern's stool?" said Grandad.

"P'raps 'ee's bin a'sittin' on it sideways!" said Grannie, "I knows a'sittin' sideways tangles yer stomach up – leastways it does wiv me!"

Grandad, who was more intelligent than Grannie, had a better idea; "I 'spects he *wants* ter sit 'im on it sideways so he can see wot's a'goin' on. If he puts a mirror on the floor he'll get a grandstand view!"

A conference was held to discuss the matter.

"How the hell are we goin' ter git it on the bus then?" said Grandad, "and wot are we a'goin' ter tell the neighbours?"

At this point, Dorrie – Grannie and Grandad's daughter, who had some knowledge of medical matters, con-

sulted a medical dictionary and came up with the answer.
"Doctor Grant," she said, "Wanted Ernie to give him a
deposit so that he could study points!"

Another factor which had great bearing on this incident
occurred at this time. Grandad was reconditioning a hoe
that he had built for tilling the soil between his broad
beans. He had great problems with this hoe. It had five
tynes, weighed all of one hundredweight, and had been
designed to be pushed. It was doubtful if a horse could
have achieved this task. In fact, Grandad almost gave
himself a hernia trying to push it. It was this tendency to
build-in design faults that continually caused Grandad
problems. He had modified the hoe so that it could be
pulled instead of pushed. Apart from Grandad constantly
falling over backwards and tearing up bean plants in the
process I suppose it could be considered a moderate success. To finish off his masterpiece, Grandad painted it. At
least he intended to, but he ran out of paint; he had half
a tin of agricultural paint in a shade of dark-brown but
ran out before completing the job.

"The next time yer gits down ter Neal's Stores,
Mother," said Grandad, "Gits me another tin of that paint
– the same as last time!"

Grannie nodded and made a mental note that the empty
tin – if given a good scrub out – would be just the ticket
in which to convey Ern's present to the doctor.

The tin was dutifully scrubbed out and Ern was given
the task of depositing his gift for the doctor. This caused
a multitude of problems, he seemed to be up in the 'little
house' all day.

"What the 'ell's 'ee up to?" moaned Grandad as the
'little house' creaked and groaned, "don't 'ee know
there's spuds ter be planted?" And when thuds and

scuffles came from within, Grandad rattled the door and enquired if he wanted any help. Apart from more wailing and moaning, the job finally seemed to be completed and Ern' appeared with paint-tin held triumphant. It was presented to Grannie to keep safe and to take to the doctor in Orpington.

So it was, on the fateful morning of Monday, 9th July, 1936, that Grannie walked from the hamlet of Maypole, over the fields to Chelsfield village, hell bent on scandal-mongering with all the other old dears that would gather in the village shop for just that purpose.

She purchased the tin of brown agricultural paint as requested by Grandad.

CHAPTER TWO

Neal's Stores

Neal's Stores was the epitome of a village shop. Its like will never be seen again. Two steps led up to a common door which opened into a general store divided into two sections.

The actual division consisted of all the things not compatible with groceries or haberdashery, namely hardware.

The hardware section would consist of: Keatings flea powder, firewood, mousetraps, Sunlight soap, Blanco for canvas plimsolls and front doorsteps, fly paper, candles, paraffin, shoe laces, Blakeys for kids shoes, buckets, Bluebell polish, chamber pots, sacks of chicken food and corn which people sat on. There would be cloth bags of Rickets blue, dog biscuits, hurricane lamps, Brilliantine, lamp wicks, wooden clothes-pegs, string and raffia, and a cabinet containing all things medical. This was a cabinet of torture, everything therein hurt! Sloane's liniment, Vick, Thermogene wool, Sulphur ointment, Snowfire cream for chilblains, corn plasters and Daisy Powder for headaches; these actually gave you headaches, not cured them. Particular emphasis seemed to be given to laxatives, these would be included in the things that hurt. Burned into our memories was the dreadful Syrup of figs, followed closely by Fynnon Salts, Andrews Liver

Salts, and Ex-Lax; a chocolate designed to trick unsuspecting children. Grannie's particular favourites were odd things called Senna Pods. These were used to make an infusion which, when used by Grannie in conjunction with any two others, made a concoction guaranteed to blow your brains out.

The bran-tub stood here at Christmas time; hopeful, snotty-nosed kids paid tuppence, and came up with penny tin whistles wrapped in coloured paper. *It was here also that decorating materials were kept, particu larly paint!*

The left side of the shop was the haberdashery department; rolls of cloth were piled high on shelves at the back. There were trays of Sylko cottons, pretty ribbons and Broderie Anglais lace collars. Rolls of oil-cloth were there in plenty, to be cut off in lengths for use as tablecloths. There was a ghastly collection of boots and faded shoes; the boots sold quickly, but the shoes, curling with age, were old and shop-soiled and would be sold off cheaply years afterwards. There was an odd Wellington boot or two, and for no known reason a solitary riding boot. There was a selection of the obligatory black caps worn as 'best' by the farm workers, and a collection of various straw hats and Boaters for the more snappy dressers of the village.

This side had a mahogany counter, polished and worn by years of use, with an unreadable brass rule. Its numerals were completely worn away by rolls of cloth that had been thumped over and over, as they were unrolled and measured; cloth always seemed to be priced at one and a penny three (one shilling and a penny three farthings) per yard.

The right side of the shop was a wonderland of every fruit imaginable. This also had a mahogany counter on which would be displayed nuts and dried fruits from Africa and the Orient; there would be brilliantly-coloured Mandarin oranges in tissue wrappers of many colours. Plump yellow lemons and Fyffes bananas with blue labels; all of which gave the store a delicious aroma. Huge Cheddar cheeses, strong and white, would be alongside a haunch of ham, on a white, china pedestal, to be carved fresh from the bone. In front of this counter, a dozen open-topped biscuit tins would display a selection of biscuits beyond your wildest dreams. Sides of oak-smoked bacon hung in line at the back. On a marble slab by the bacon, amongst jars of Marmite, Bovril, and Oxo and Juvis gravy cubes, stood the pride of the grocers shop – the bacon slicer. This was a stain-less-steel wonder with spikes, enamelled in fire-engine red. This was operated with a flourish by Mr Boswick the owner, who was the only person allowed to use it; sadly his heavily bandaged fingers belied his ability in this direction.

The floor of the whole shop was thick with sawdust; this not only gave the whole place a comforting snugness when you walked in, but, according to Grandad, soaked up the blood from Mr Boswick's cut fingers.

The shop was really run by two ladies, Mrs Boswick, the wife of the owner, and a Mrs Wilcox, both of these were cronies of Grannie, who would refer to them as 'them gals', who would send her not one, *but two* incredible cakes at Christmas. These were as a token of their appreciation for her custom throughout the year.

Grannie only fell out with them one one occasion!

We could only afford to buy broken biscuits from the village shop; these were part of Grannie's weekly order, and were delivered by Bob Hogben; the delivery boy employed by Mr Boswick.

Outside deliveries were Mr Boswick's particular forté. He was in charge of paraffin deliveries and the bane of Bog Hogben the unfortunate employee whose job it was to deliver the paraffin. Being the main carrier, Bob was made to pedal for miles. That was bad enough, but when twenty-two gallons, in one gallon cans, had to be delivered on a Monday to the Tomkin household at Woodlands – and ten cans in the carrier made things unstable – it was a chore that took the biscuit.

That was not the only thing to take the biscuit. Whilst the paraffin run was a dread to contemplate, an untold delight was a grocery round involving calls to Grannie Packham at *Yewtree House*, Mrs Wright at the *Rock and Fountain*, and Mrs Exall on Well Hill. The only problem was that Grannie Packham, in company with these other two customers, had a vague feeling of unease, that she seemed to be paying more each week for a diminishing amount of broken biscuits.

It was this point that caused Grannie Packham to raise hell in the village shop, and to return the tin of brown, agricultural paint she had bought earlier that day.

Grandad, thinking that it would take Grannie some time to buy his paint, had asked his old friend, Walter Winchcombe, to get him a tin from the village shop. Consequently, he ended up with two tins, and asked Grannie to return the one that she had purchased.

Grannie, in order to kill two birds with one stone, took Grandad's new tin, and brother Ern's present for the doctor in the same basket.

After having a row with the two old girls in the village shop about her broken biscuits, and telling them that she was not made of money and to have their scales checked,

Grannie replaced Grandad's tin of paint on the shelf where the paint was kept, and proceeded to the bus stop to take the 477 bus that ran from the village to Orpington. Doctor Grant's surgery was only minutes from Orpington War Memorial, and Grannie was able to catch the return bus, feeling that it had been a job well done.

It was what happened next that caused the problem!
Grannie had a letter from the doctor!

CHAPTER THREE

Painting the Clouds with Sunshine

It is odd how unknown details of past events eventually come to light with the passage of time.

Fifty years after Grannie's argument with the old girls at the village shop over the short weight in her biscuit order, Bob Hogben and I were discussing his job as delivery boy at Neal's Stores. Apart from his admission that it was he who pinched Grannie's biscuits; he also owned up to having Mrs Wright's and Mrs Exalls as well!

The felony was compounded, as not only did he pilfer their broken biscuits, but he gladly accepted a tip of a shilling from all three of them, as a payment for services rendered!

It was Bob who reminded me of the awful rumpus that blew up three weeks after Grannie received the letter from Doctor Grant, between Bert Parks, the landlord of the *Five Bells* in Chelsfield, and the old girls at the village shop.

Doctor Grant's letter to Grannie was short and to the point:

12th July, 1936

Dear Mrs Packham,
 I am in receipt of a sample for analysis in relation to Ernest Packham. On examination it would appear

25

that Ernest Packham either has a severe turpentine contamination, or linseed-oil poisoning.

I suspect the latter; either that, or the container that you left with me really does contain agricultural brown paint.

Would you please collect this specimen and deposit it elsewhere.

Sincerely,
Dr F. W. Grant

To say that this letter caused consternation would be the understatement of the year.

Grannie and Grandad held a conference in the orchard.

"Wot the 'ell's 'ee on about?" said Grandad.

"Silly ol' devil's a'gettin' mixed up! said Grannie.

"All I know's," said Grandad, "Is I've got a tin of paint that Walter got me, and you took the other back ter the shop, so wot the 'ell's 'ee got?"

Grannie gulped and said in a plaintive voice, "Well, I tooks two tins in me bag, one I gives back ter the shop, and t'other I takes ter the doctor, so wot's bein a'goin' on?"

Grandad sniffed and said cockily "I tells yer wot's bin a'goin' on, Mother. If I've got a tin of paint, and the doctor's got a tin of paint, it don't take too much brainpower ter work out where the other's gorn!"

Grannie said with great apprehension, "wot do yer mean, Will?"

And Grandad replied, "Bloody top-me, woman, it's as plain as the nose on yer face, you put Ern's present fer the doctor back on the shelf in the bloody shop!

Grannie started to wring her hands in panic, "Gawd!" she said, "wot's ter be done now, Will?"

And Grandad replied "Well, I tell yer wot 'ent goin' ter

be done! I 'ent a'goin' back ter the shop ter ask fer Ern's tin o'poop back! Best yer fergits all about it an' we'll see wot 'appens.

So, Grannie and Grandad sat back in an embarrassed silence, and waited for events to unfold – and unfold they did!

Grandad had collected the tin of suspect paint from the receptionist at the doctors' surgery in Orpington. He stammered an apology and said that as brother Ern had now recovered, there was no need for any further investigation. He scuttled out, feeling guilty, and was soon on the bus back to Chelsfield. He had decided to try to surreptitiously slip the correct tin of paint back on the shelf in the shop, whilst looking for Ern's rogue tin in the process.

Sadly he was too late. The first sign of trouble was when Grandad got off the 477 bus in Chelsfield village.

The colour scheme of the *Five Bells* public house in Chelsfield village was cream and brown. Everything above the damp course was cream – everything below was brown. It had been pointed out to Bert Parks by several of his saloon-bar clientele, that the brown paint at the front of the pub was being scuffed badly by public-bar customers leaning their bicycles against it: it made the pub look scruffy, they said.

Bert Parks, above all, was a saloon-bar man. It was general knowledge that he considered himself only worthy of associating with the halves-of-bitter brigade that frequented the saloon bar. If a complaint came from that quarter, then it was given top priority and attended to immediately. Principle prevented Bert Parks from serving in the public bar. That task was left to a jovial barman of ruddy countenance named Albert Mills.

Bert Parks was uncrowned mayor of Chelsfield. He was loud, full of bluster, and as cunning as they came, indeed, he had a large cage with a captive monkey at the rear of the pub, to entertain summer visitors taking refreshment on the back lawn. Grannie said that he was as "Sharp as a wagon-load of his monkeys, packed arse uppards!" (Whatever that meant!)

It was he, each year, who regularly donated a porker to be bowled for at the local fête; it was also he who managed to regularly win it!

The locals caught on to this wheeze and refused to compete, leaving Bert to bask in the admiration of his great generosity, and to wonder at his success in constantly winning back his own pig! It all added to the air of benevolence that he radiated, in pursuance of eminence in the community.

His bearing added to the illusion; he was large, with a commanding air. He normally wore a heavy, brown, three-piece suit, with a waistcoat heavily adorned with a gold Albert watch and chain gracing an ample paunch. This would be displayed almost as if a mayoral chain of office. He had a tendency to have a florid complexion, which on occasions turned purple. When Grandad got off the 477 bus at Chelsfield, Bert Parks was purple.

"Christ!" said Grandad to Grannie sometime later. "You should 'ave seen ol' Bert. I 'ent never seen anythin' like it!"

"Wot's 'ee bin on about then?" said Grannie.

"Reckon 'ee's bin painting the clouds wiv sunshine, and 'ent lookin' none too pleased about it, either!" said Grandad. "Regular fired up 'ee was. Christ! Talk about bloody purple. I thought 'ee was goin' ter bust!"

Bob Hogben said his shouting was audible the length

of the High Street; he had a brush and a tin of paint in his hands at the time. He was breathing fire and thunder.

Grannie asked with some trepidation, "Wot's this all about then, father?"

Grandad replied, "Wot's this all about? You bloody well know wot it's all about! You've left brother Ern's visiting card at the shop, that's wot!

Grannie pursed her lips and said in a mealy-mouthed way, "It's me poor ol' eyes. I can't see so well now that the nights is a'drawin' in."

Grandad continued, "What are yer on about woman, it's bloody July! An' there ent nuffink wrong wiv yer eyes when it comes ter countin' yer 'ousekeepin' munney! Christ! Woz 'ee shouting!"

There was a vague rivalry between Bert Parks and the old girls at the village shop. It was all to do with who commanded the focal point of the village. While the *Five Bells* held claim to this title during licensing hours, it must be said that with all the village housewives scandal-mongering in the shop all day long, Neal's Stores ran him a very close second. There was also a certain amount of acid, because Bert obtained his sundry food items from elsewhere and undercut the village shop; no opportunity was ever lost by either combatant to get one over the other.

While it was not exactly gold that Bert struck that day, by the advantage that he made of it, he might as well have!

In front of a host of customers he triumphantly held up his brush and tin of paint and bellowed, "You've pulled some bloody smart capers in yer time, but I'm buggered if this time you've gorn too far!"

Mrs Boswick, who was normally quite able to shut anyone up with a look, gave Bert Parks the sort of withering glare that she would normally have reserved for something the cat brought in. "Kindly lower your voice, Mr Parks," she said. "I find your tone offensive!"

Her choice of words was not good. Bert Parks said, "If yer find my tone offensive, then wot the 'ell do yer find this!" And giving emphasis to his words, he waved the offending brush and tin under Mrs Boswick's nose. Mrs Boswell staggered backwards and, rapidly fanning her face with her hand said, "Good God! Mr Parks, whatever have you been doing with that?"

Bert Parks replied indignantly, "Painting me bloody pub with it, wot do you think?"

Mrs Boswell said, "What an odd paint to use, Mr Parks. Wherever did you get it?"

Bert Parks replied, "Well, to start with, I bought it in your bloody shop, and it 'ent paint, it's poop!"

There was a cross-section of lady customers in the shop at the time, the more refined of them hastily withdrew with saintly smiles, the coarser elements let loose guffaws of laughter and made rude remarks; none of which pleased either Mrs Boswell or Mr Parks.

Bert Parks slammed his suspect tin of paint on the provisions counter. This caused Mrs Boswell to shriek, "Not on my provisions counter *please* Mr Parks!"

To which Bert Parks replied, his face red with anger, "If yer don't like it on yer food counter, Mrs Boswick, how do you think I like it all over me bloody pub!"

With that, Bert swept out majestically, leaving the old girls and Mr Boswell to hold a court of enquiry as to how such a thing could have happened. They finally decided that the paint manufacturer was to blame, and after a stern letter of complaint, obtained their supplies elsewhere.

They took a new tin over to Bert Parks who told them what they could do with it.

Later, when he was scrubbing the wall of the *Five Bells* with a broom and hot water, he was asked by a mischievous neighbour what had made him suspect that his paint was not up to it's usual quality? Bert Parks snarled back that he had painted out several scuff marks earlier in the morning, but a slight shower two hours later had washed the damned stuff off!

Grandad, who revelled in having something to moan about, could not get over the enormity of it all.

"Don't know wot possessed yer, woman," he said to Grannie. "Jest as well they didn't recognise the tin. And look at the trouble you've caused. Yer damn nearly blew Ern inside-out, dragged the doctor up 'ere without reason, made Bert Parks and the old gals have a bloody good row, caused them ter close their account wiv the paint makers, and ter top it all, damn nearly got me caught tryin' ter smuggle the tin back in the shop!"

Grannie kept very quiet – she had good reason – apart from complaining bitterly to the old girls about being short-changed in her broken-biscuit order, she had also obtained a refund for Ern's returned tin of brown agricultural paint.

Grannie and old Mrs Swift placed the one shilling and tuppence refund on a horse called 'Reubens Return' in the three-thirty at Cheltenham the following Saturday. It won, and Grannie came into the princely sum of one guinea. The greatest sum that she had ever had. She said that it was an omen; Reubens was a painter and she returned the paint – so it had to win!

CHAPTER FOUR

A Time of Happiness

It is difficult to describe the way of life on our patch at Maypole. Our land occupied about two acres. It was divided in two by a Yew hedge that was six feet high and four feet wide. It was one hundred yards long, and ran from north to south. It had several openings that led from one part of the garden to the other.

There was no particular plan or organisation to the lay-out of things. There were three collections of assorted apple trees that we liked to call orchards, but in reality they were nothing more than very small collections of apple trees that were the sum total of Grandad's efforts at grafting.

The rest of the garden was divided into various-sized plots, in which Grandad and his awful brother, Ern, would cultivate the masses of vegetables that we consumed each year. Dotted about, for no particular reason, or logic, were gooseberry, blackcurrant, and rhubarb patches. There were Blackjack, Weedon, River, Tzaar, Victoria, Damson, and Yellow plum trees. There were three Worcester apple trees; and even an apple tree that had five varieties growing on it. There was one William and three Conference pear trees, and a multitude of greengages for good measure. When patches of horse radish, wild sage, bundles of chives, mint and parsley, and delicious land cress that burnt like mustard was added, it resulted in a hotch-potch of flavours beyond belief.

Grandad and his brother Ern tilled the land and grew the vegetables. They would both dig vast areas of garden by hand, and plant early, main crop, and late potatoes. These would provide our supplies for the year. There would be ample rows of Brussels sprouts, purple sprouting broccoli, Savoy-drumhead cabbages, and parsnips and carrots that were kept in the ground all year long. Rows of leeks, onions and celery would be eaten raw with great slabs of strong Cheddar cheese. Grandad grew salad crops that were beyond belief. I have never seen such red winter lettuces, with butter-coloured hearts, or such sweet beetroot, not only eaten as a salad accompaniment, but also in a great tureen, smothered in butter, as a winter vegetable. He grew small, dark-red tomatoes with a sweetness and flavour that has gone forever. We lived on the fat of the land.

At least we did when Grandad had a job. In the depression of the thirties, things became difficult. There were plenty of vegetables but very little protein. Grandad shot a few rabbits, but cartridges were expensive. He designed a bird trap with an ash sieve propped up with a stick; a long piece of string tied to the stick at one end and leading to Grannie sitting in the back doorway at the other. A handful of corn was sprinkled under the sieve and the trap was set. It worked like magic. My mother could remember Grandad and Grannie plucking birds until the early hours, and the unforgettable flavour of a huge pie that really did contain four-and-twenty blackbirds.

So Grandad, who had been head butler to Squire Waring at Woodlands, taught himself woodwork and eventually became a master carpenter. When things became difficult he became self-employed and contracted himself out to various builders as a jobbing carpenter. Apart from this, he was in charge of the garden, and brother Ern was the labourer.

It was at this difficult time that a neighbour, Walter Winchcombe, spotted a rabbit amongst the gooseberry bushes in our garden. He crept stealthily round to our open front door and gave Grandad the tip that our Sunday lunch was eating the gooseberries. Grandad, just awake from a nap, quickly loaded the 12-bore shotgun that stood behind the front door. He and Walter formulated a plan. Walter would go to the end of the gooseberry patch and drive the rabbit out into the open, and Grandad – waiting near to Walter's boundary hedge, would bag him as he broke cover. However, the best laid plans of mice and men never quite work out. As Walter kicked up a racket walking up the gooseberry rows, so the first thing to come out was our dog, Jip, tail between the legs, hotly pursued by the rabbit.

Grandad shouted, "Damn and blast the bloody dog!"

Walter shrieked, "Let em' both go, Will!"

Grandad shouted, "Wot, the dog and the rabbit?"

"No!" bellowed and excited Walter. "Both bleeding barrels!"

And Grandad did! There was a colossal explosion as his feet came off the ground; he was enveloped in a cloud of black smoke. Fortunately he missed everything in sight – except the rear of the outside lavatory!

The outside lavatory, also known as 'the little house', was a refuge of its own, it was a place of tranquillity in which to contemplate life. It was a place where we all, from time to time, sat in oblivion with the door wide open, studying the various plants that grew in the orchard, and listening to the birdsong that graced the summer evenings.

Sadly, it was Grandad's brother, Ern, who on that occasion happened to be sitting in the little house doing some contemplating.

The little house was a substantial building. It was constructed of heavy timber with ship-lapped weatherboarding; it was tarred and had a heavy Kentish peg-tiled roof. It was a two-seater, with a heavy wooden flap at the back which gave access to the bucket. It was this that Grandad shot to pieces!

The one fortunate thing about this incident was that Ern was stone deaf. This was just as well, because the clatter that the buckshot made as it tore through the wooden flap and punched twenty-two holes in the bucket must have been deafening.

Ern never heard a thing, he never knew how lucky he was to have avoided serious injury by inches. The only observation he made, was to note the holes in the bucket. Grandad, ever the silver-tongued charmer, managed to persuade him that it was corrosion. He did a crafty repair job with a packet of pot-menders that he kept for repairing Grannie's saucepans. Sadly, these gave the bucket a hedgehog-like appearance. They were a constant reminder to Grandad of the time that he had missed a rabbit by ten feet, and nearly shot a sitting duck!

Grandad had a Victorian attitude to life. Everyone sat at the table for Sunday lunch whilst he, as head of the family, carved the joint. This was a ceremony performed with a flourish. first, the carving knife had to be sharpened. Grandad would show everyone how it should be done. It was, he said, important to have great flexibility in the wrist. He would qualify this by holding the arm rigid, whilst waggling the hand that held the knife back and forth at great speed. This would be accomplished in an unbearably cocky manner. While still furiously waggling the knife back and forth he would advance the sharpening-steel until the two came into contact. Grandad would then make an extremely loud click-clacking noise while he banged the two together. We would all wait with great irritation, as the food grew cold, for the performance to end so that we could eat. All he seemed to do was to blunt the knife and mangle the joint in the carving process.

Happily the whole ritual came to an end, when his flying knife cut through the string of a five pound suet pudding that Grannie was carrying through to the pantry. The whole thing collapsed in an uncontrollable mush of half cooked dough. It did not seem possible that so much pudding could have come from the severing of a single piece of string. There was suet pudding everywhere.

Granny flew at Grandad in what Grandad thought was an unreasonable rage. "Now look wot you've gorn an' bloody well done!" she said, "A standin' showin' orf wiv that damn sharpenin' steel! I don't knows why the 'ell yer 'as ter does it at mealtimes!"

Grandad, humbled, said lamely, "If you'd a'cooked it more it wouldn't 'ave fallen orf the plate."

An' if you 'adn't bin a'swishin' about wiv the knife it wouldn't be all over the damn floor!" she replied, snottily.

Grandad sat down and ate his lunch, leaving Grannie – as he always did – to clean up the mess. He even pointed out with his fork the bit that she had missed that was stuck to the table leg. He was very lucky not to be hit with the remains as she passed by on her way to the dust-bin.

A testy silence lasted throughout the meal and long into the afternoon. He never again sharpened the carving knife at mealtimes.

It may be gathered by this, that Grandad was small in stature, Victorian in outlook, and considered himself head of the household. He was also cocky, light-fingered, and liked his wallop. It would not be untrue to say that he was also extremely clever, self-taught, and prone to the odd flight of fancy.

His brother, Ern, was none of these things. All that could be said for him was that he was dim-witted and small-minded. Grannie considered him to be obsessed with sex because he regularly read the back page of her womens magazines. As none ever came his way, he could hardly be blamed for that!

Poor Ern spent his years either living with us at the old cottage, or with his sister, my Great Aunt Eliza, at Bucks Cross; it all depended on whom he had fallen out with at the time. It suited Grandad, being the artful dodger, for Ern to stay at our place; his sixteen shillings a week for his lodgings made Grannie happy, and being left all the menial work to do in the garden, made Grandad *very* happy. It was, in Grandad's eyes, a very acceptable arrangement. The fact that Ern completely took over Grannie's side of the fireplace on cold winter nights was, however, an arrangement doomed to disaster. From time to time he and Grannie would have a good old dust-up. This would result in his moving back to Bucks Cross. This seemed to happen, much to Grandad's vexation, every three years.

Grannie was as tough as old boots (she had to be); it was she that staggered all over the cobbles bringing the buckets of coal in for the fire. It was she that did the washing-up at the outside sink, with ice-cold water and a block of cracked, latherless Fairy soap. When this is done in a force-ten gale with frozen snow-flakes tearing your skin like razor blades, then one had to be tough or die from exposure.

Grannie seemed to extend this toughness to other things. Her feet would be regularly attacked with Grandad's electric pliers. After soaking them in water hot enough to take the skin off, and containing enough mustard to inflict first-degree burns, Grannie would attack her toe-nails with a vengeance. The cats would scatter from the danger of flying clippings, and Grandad would comment that all should keep clear, "'Cos Mother's up to 'er larks, and we don't all want ter git bloody blinded do we?" He would also complain when she attacked her corns with his pruning knife.

"Why does yer 'ave ter do that when I'm 'avin' me bloody dinner?" He would complain, his face screwed up in disgust. "It's enough ter puts yer orf yer food!" He would conveniently forget that one minute before, when we had all been sitting down to tea, he had flung his legs in the air, sneezed, farted, slapped his thigh, and shouted, all at the same time, and all over the food table!

Grannie also over-did things with the coal-hammer. Should she find any particularly large lumps in the buckets of coal that she had brought in, they would be attacked with vigour. Grannie had her own special hammer for this purpose, it had a heavy snout at one end, and a six inch spike at the other. Grandad would sit and wince. "Christ!" he would say at the thuds coming from the pantry, "'ark at that bloody lot! Can't she tap it instead of bloody pulverisin' it!" I'll be the poor bugger that 'as ter repair the floor, not 'er!"

Grandad got no sympathy from us. He should have broken up the coal, not Grannie. All we complained about was the amount of coal that got in the vegetables. It was either coal, soot from the chimney, or chalk from the kettle, either way, one got no change from Grannie, "you've got ter eats a bushel of dirt afore yer dies," she would say. It was just one of the things that made up life in the old cottage. You ate your greens, prayed that you would find nothing, but picked out the soot, coal or chalk if you did.

In spite of it all, Grannie was the kindest, most hard-working soul that I have ever known. We all loved her more than we could every say. Her like will never be seen again.

All the women in the household were frightened of mice. Because the cats were all over-fed by Grannie, the mice became a pest. A deputation confronted Grandad; because they spent so much time standing on chairs holding their skirts up and screaming blue murder, Grandad had *got* to do something about it! Because we all had a thing about cruelty to animals, it had to be humane in its operation.

Grandad sat with pencil and paper, sketching things out as he designed his humane mousetrap. All of the next day the sounds of banging and sawing came from the shed, these were interspersed with exclamations of "Christ! Damn and blast the bloody thing!" Or "Ouch! Now I've gorn and broke me bloody finger!" finally all was completed, and we were invited to view his work of art.

Grandad's patent humane mousetrap consisted of three planks of wood nailed together to form a gully. The bottom piece was balanced in the centre like a see-saw. Suspended above this was a baulk of timber that must have been twenty pounds in weight. Grandad said that its operation was simplicity itself. He said that the mouse walked along the plank to reach the bait that was placed at the far end. When the plank over-balanced and did its see-saw bit, it released the baulk of timber which rapidly dispatched the mouse in a pain-free way!

"Stand back," he said, "I'll show you 'ow it works."

Setting it all up, he used his fingers to simulate the passage of a mouse hell bent on nicking bread from Grannie's larder.

"First,' he said, "The little bleeder comes a'walkin' up 'ere, a'lookin' fer mother's bread. 'Ah-ha', 'ee says, seein' it 'angin' at the end of the tunnel, 'lets go an' 'ave a look!'."

At this point, Grandad made a walking action with his index and middle fingers, up the ramp and over the 'see-saw'. What happened next was too awful to behold. The trap triggered. The baulk of timber slammed, with an awful crash, down on Grandad's unsuspecting fingers!

"Bloody top me!" Yelped Grandad at Grannie, at the same time trying to get his hand out of the trap, "Wot the hell did yer do that fer?"

"I 'ent done nuffink," said Grannie. "You was the one that was playin' at mices, not me! I was only watchin'."

"You knocked the bloody thing as I was a'puttin' me 'and inside," said an irate Grandad, still trying to get his hand out.

A guilty Grannie said "I woz only tryin' ter 'elp by pushin' the cheese towards yer fingers."

Grandad had by now managed to extricate his badly bruised fingers. He stood there blowing them furiously. "When I wants yer bloody 'elp, I'll ask fer it!" He said, "Christ! It don't 'arf bloody-well hurt!"

Grannie said, "It shouldn't, it's supposed ter be humane 'ent it?"

Grandad glared as if he could have struck her dead and said, "Wot yer got between yer bloody ears, woman, how can yer knock a mices bloody brains out without hurtin' 'im; although on second thoughts if I stuck your damn 'ead in there and triggered the bloody thing, I reckon yer wouldn't feel a thing! That's 'cos there 'ent no bloody brains ter knock out!"

Discretion being the better part of valour, we quickly dispersed and left them to it. Later in the evening, Grandad set up his trap against the wall behind the bureau, and the events of the day were forgotten. Grandad sat with his squashed fingers in a basin of warm water and moaned all evening. We were all sitting listening to the nine o'clock news on the radio, when the trap went off. An awful scream came from beneath the bureau. Grandad had caught the cat! In the course of time, he caught all five of them. None were badly injured – severely shaken perhaps – and cross-eyed for a day or two, but as Grandad said, "Curiosity 'ent never killed a cat! Bloody well shakes 'em up a bit, but never kills 'em!"

Grannie finally used the trap for the last time when she tried to spy on a passing neighbours hat from behind the lace curtains. She stuck her foot in it. She ended up with a blue toe and a black toe-nail. Her language could be described as colourful. "Damn and blast the bloody thing!" she said, as she hurled the lot on the fire. Grandad kept his head down – he hid behind his news-paper and made no comment.

It would be reasonable to say that Grannie had a cross to bear with all of us. With Grandad and his brother Ern, it was Grandad's penchant for the bottle, and the fact that both of them lay spread out on either side of the fireplace, blocking her only access to the cooking pots. They both expected to be waited on at all times, and Grannie did the waiting. At no time did they do anything to make her life easier.

Grannie had problems with her two daughters as well. Dorrie lost her husband through an accident on the railways. Little Nell lost hers through having to find work abroad at the time of the depression. They both finally came home to *Yewtree House* to live with the old people. That was bad enough, but they both brought their unruly kids with them!

That was where Bryan and I came in. We spent our time running wild in the fields of Kent. When we were not doing that, we were either leading Grannie up hill and down dale, or tormenting the life out of Grandad's brother Ern.

Grannie's lot in the year of 1937 was to look after five adults, two children, a dog, five cats, several chickens, and a rabbit. By then she was the wrong side of sixty-five. She should have been taking things easier. She also had problems with Grandad's dog, 'Trimmer'!

CHAPTER FIVE

Trimmer

In his time, Grandad had four dogs, an Irish Terrier, appropriately named Patsy, who, for no known reason, would either fight the back door or bite Grandad; He had a Jack Russell named Spot, who had a patch on one eye. Spot was inherited from Grandad's brother, Ern. He would craftily nip Grannie's foot as she walked by. Then there was Jip, who was really Grannie's dog. She would rush about with a show of aggression and disappear like a streak of light at the sight of a rabbit.

There was also Trimmer. Trimmer was a cross between a Labrador and something else. He was a large, black dog who would follow Grandad about as if on an errand of great importance. He had no sense of humour. He would never play with a ball like other dogs. He would only play with Grannie. At least, we thought that he was playing, but Trimmer was not playing, he was deadly serious! Grandad, who had no pretensions when it came to the niceties of life, would look at the dog and say "looks like the ol' boy is a'gittin' frisky!" The signs were obvious, and we would all choose to look the other way. Grandad would keep harping on about it. "Christ! Look at the ol' bugger!" he would say, "there's life in the ol' dog yet – best locks up yer daughters I say!" In Grandad's case he should have said lock up your wives!"

Trimmer, who normally ignored Grannie at all other times, would suddenly, at springtime, become most attentive. He would follow her about, studying her every move – waiting for her to scrub the floor.

It was at this point, when she was on her hands and knees working up a lather, that Trimmer would throw decorum to the winds, and lose control!

The trouble was that Grannie was small. When she was on her hands and knees she was at Trimmer's height – that was the attraction.

The first time this happened, Grannie was scrubbing the floor by the bureau. She had been using the flap as an ironing board and it was still in the down position. She said afterwards that she did not know what possessed the dog. One minute she was scrubbing hard, and the next she received a bump up the back. This knocked her beret over her eyes, the ash off her cigarette, and gave her a nasty bump on the head as she leaped up and hit the flap of the bureau. Grannie was not happy, she complained bitterly to Grandad.

"Don't a'knows wot Trimmer's about," she said, "keeps wantin' ter play. 'Ee 'ent never done that afore!" Grandad, a wise old owl, said nothing.

When this happened twice more the following day, Grannie became even more irate. "I've 'ad enough of this, Father!" She said. "I've hit 'im with the broom and set about 'im wiv the fly swat, but it don't seem ter make no difference. I don't know, and maybe I've got the wrong end of the stick, but I reckon as how 'ee's got a bit of courtin' in mind!"

Grandad kept very quiet, he could see the danger signs.

Once Grannie got the bit between her teeth she was difficult to stop; particularly when Trimmer had tried to take advantage of her, when she had been bending over to pick up some coal that had dropped from the coal bucket.

Grannie broke the awful news that Grandad knew was coming, but hoped he would never hear. "Father!" she said, "I'm goin' ter gives yer the money, and yer a'goin' ter take the dog down ter Pratts Bottom, and git the vet ter 'ave 'im seen to!"

Grandad paled and said, "Yer can't mean it! 'Ee's too bloody old. It ent right! Damn it all, woman, would you 'ave me seen to, jest 'cos I gits frisky at times?"

"It's not that, Father." said Grannie. "You're past it, and 'ee ent! I don't 'ave ter keep a'lookin' backwards at you, I daresn't take me eyes orf 'im! Anyway, I ent 'avin' no more of it, either you takes 'im, or I does!"

At ten o'clock the next Saturday morning, a sad Grandad and an unsuspecting Trimmer, wandered off over the fields to Chelsfield. The intention was to pass through the village and take the lane past the church and on down to Pratts Bottom. It was a long way – probably a round trip of five miles, and Grandad was weary before he had even got to the village. He stopped at the *Five Bells* for some refreshment.

It was while in this genial hostelry that Grandad met his old friend, George Humble. He bemoaned the unfortunate lot that had overtaken them. "There was no way," he said, "that he wanted ter walk all the bloody way ter Pratts Bottom and back, and no way that he wanted ter spend all that money ter make his ol' friend lose 'is manhood!"

George Humble was resourceful if nothing else. He and Grandad got together in the corner. There was much nodding and tapping of noses, the odd sly wink and nudge, and apart from Grandad nipping over the road for a brief visit to Neal's Stores, nothing else really happened.

That was not strictly true, a lot happened. Grandad and George Humble went on a bender. Grandad spent the money that Grannie had given him for the vet on a great deal of mild and bitter. They staggered out of the *Five Bells* at a quarter-to-three in the afternoon, very much the worse for wear.

He and George wobbled off across the fields until they came to the field by Albert Blott's house. It was then that Grandad produced his purchase from the village shop. It was quite simply an ordinary one-inch bandage, three feet long. He and George, with great difficulty, then proceeded to do a bandaging job on Trimmer.

A while later Grannie heard Grandad and George Humble at the garden gate. Grandad was hanging on to George with his hat on sideways. "Christ, George," he said, "I'd never 'ave made it without yer."

George Humble, noting Grannie at the front door, said, "You did all the work, Will, you carried 'im! All I did woz gives yer some support!" And looking at Grannie he said, "You'd better give 'im a drink, Ellie, he's bloody worn out!"

Grannie was concerned to think that Grandad had carried the dog all the way from Pratts Bottom, but as Grandad had said, there was no way that the poor animal could have walked. Grannie poured Grandad a large whisky from the bottle that she kept purely for medicinal purposes, and wondered at the effect that it had on him. He appeared to be paralytic. She put it down to exhaustion.

Trimmer did not seem unduly bothered by his major surgery. As Grandad said, "the vet made an impressive job of bandaging his wedding tackle; he even finished it orf with a bloody bow."

Trimmer did not seem to like it very much. It seemed to spoil his image. As Grandad said to George Humble, "It might make him look like a bloody pansy, mincing about like that, but rather 'ee looks like that, than being tuppence short of a shillin'."

Grannie gave Trimmer the top brick off the chimney. He lived the life of Riley. He was not allowed to exert himself, and was tucked into his basket at night with one of Mr Smallwood's meat pies. Grandad watched him like a hawk, at any signs of amorous intent he was taken up the garden for a walk. Grannie wondered at the complete lack of a scar when the bandage fell off? Grandad said "That's wot yer pays good money ter the vet fer!"

CHAPTER SIX

A Drop of Scotch

There was another occasion when a sample was wanted by the doctor for analysis. Only this time there was no mix up. It was a straightforward case of Ern getting up at all hours of the night, and waking up the entire house.

When you lived in a five-hundred year old, traditional Kentish country cottage, with two massive bedrooms, in which everyone slept – which were connected by a single door, it was difficult, when attending to calls of nature, not to wake everyone up.

As usual, Ern refused to seek medical advice. It was Grannie who caught the bus to Orpington and talked things over with the doctor. From Grannie's description of Ern's symptoms, the doctor said that he suspected an excess of sugar. He requested Grannie to obtain a sample of Ern's water.

As with the paint tin, the problem was finding the receptacle in which to convey the sample to the surgery. This time, Grandad found the answer.

When he had arrived back at the old cottage in an exhausted state with Trimmer, it was Grannie that had revived him with a drop of medicinal whisky. The truth of the matter was, that when she had looked the other way, he had drained the last drop. The empty bottle provided the means to convey Ern's problem to the doctor, and Grandad, complete with carrier bag, was the carrier.

Grandad did his usual thing and intentionally missed the bus. This meant that he had to stroll over the fields to catch the 477 bus from the village. It also meant that with an hour to wait, he had ample time for refreshment in the *Five Bells*.

Grandad had a merry old time with Albert Mills, the jovial barman of the Public Bar. Albert Mills had a lady friend named Grace King; the three of them consumed a vast amount of mild and bitter.

Grandad had a questionable escort in the shape of Albert and Grace. They lifted him, in a fashion, on the bus, and saw him on his merry way.

It was when the time came to alight at the War Memorial in Orpington, that Grandad found that he had mislaid his carrier bag. Apart from himself, the bus had been empty for the entire length of his journey; he deduced that he must have left it in the pub.

Catching the same bus on its return, Grandad enquired if the conductor had seen his missing carrier bag; he was told that as it had not been handed in, it could not have been left on the bus. The carrier bag was still where he had left it (by the door of the public bar) in the *Five Bells*. There was, however, one omission – someone had stolen Ern's bottle of vintage whisky! Grandad said nothing. He was not proud of the fact that he was the carrier of such a burden – it would have made him the laughing stock of the village. He wended his way home across the fields and told Grannie that the doctor could find nothing wrong. He said that Ern had to drink plenty of water and eat an apple a day. Grandad hoped that the apple a day would keep the doctor away, and the water would effect a cure.

It was a few days later that Grandad, in company with George Humble, was propping up the bar at the *Bo-Peep*.

"I'm buggered if I 'ent seen the bloody lot now, George!" he said.

"That's a pretty strong statement ter make out with, Will!" said George, in reply. "Wot's this all about, then?"

"I stopped orf at the *Bells* on me way to Orpington last week, and left me carrier bag behind." said Grandad.

"That 'ent too much of a world shakin' event," said George. "I'm a doin' such things all the time!"

"It 'ent that," said Grandad. "I'm buggered if someone pinched a present I wos a'takin' ter someone in Orpington fer Ernie."

"Did yer report it?" asked George

"Couldn't find no one to report it to." Grandad replied.

"Well, you're in luck!" said George. "I can see Constable Tanner a'comin' along the lane on his bike; I'll give 'im a shout!"

Before Grandad could stop him, George Humble was at the door and shouting to Constable Tanner. "Oi, Jack!" he called, "got a case fer yer ter investigate in 'ere!"

Constable Tanner stopped outside the pub. To be called upon to actually investigate a crime, was a rare occurrence indeed. In fact, it had never happened before. He swelled with importance. Adopting his most sinister, hawk-like look, he said "Hello, hello, hello. Wot 'ave we got 'ere, then?"

George Humble said "We've 'ad a crime most foul committed, and we thinks yer ought ter sort it out."

"When it comes ter crime," said the awful Jack, "I'm yer man."

Taking out his notebook with a flourish, and wetting

the end of his pencil with his tongue, he said, "Right, what happened, then?"

"Well," said George, "It didn't exactly 'appen 'ere, and someone pinched a carrier bag!"

Constable Tanner looked narked, this was obviously not going to be a case for the Crown Court, indeed it would probably not even raise eyebrows at the local police station.

Testily, he asked, "You stopped me from a'goin' about police business fer a bleedin' paper bag that was pinched somewhere else?"

"Not exactly!" said George. "It belonged ter Will Packham, and it weren't the bag, it woz 'is brother Ern's present inside it!"

"Wot was that then?" said Constable Tanner.

George Humble turned to Grandad inside the bar and said, "Wot woz Ern's present then, Will?"

An embarrassed Grandad said, "it was a sort of bottle of whisky."

"Wot's that supposed to mean?" said Constable Tanner, "either it's a bottle of whisky, or it 'ent!"

Grandad shuffled his feet and said, "Well, let's say it were a whisky bottle then."

Constable Tanner now looked decidedly apprehensive.

"Well," he said, "an empty bottle 'ent much fer anyone ter nick."

"Well, that's the trouble," replied Grandad. "It weren't empty."

Constable Tanner became agitated. In a slightly high-pitched voice he said, "Wot was in the bloody bottle then?"

And Grandad, with all the impact of an atom bomb said, "It were a bottle of Ern's piddle I woz takin' ter the doctor in Orpington!"

The change in Constable Tanner's manner was remarkable. "Christ!" he said, hastily flinging his leg over his bicycle, "this 'ere lot's bloody serious! I'd better git down ter the station and report it."

Despite Grandad calling after him that "It don't matter, I kin allus git Ern ter fill up another bottle!" there was no stopping Constable Tanner. He pedalled off towards Bucks Cross as if his very life depended on it. *Which indeed it did!*

It transpired that Constable Tanner had never got on particularly well with his mother-in-law. In fact it had been hate at first sight. This was a continual bone of contention with his wife, who constantly being piggy-in-the-middle tried to keep the peace between them.

It was she who saw what appeared to be a bottle of whisky under her husbands cape. Caught with his trousers down so-to-speak, Constable Tanner said in a moment of panic, that as she had been on at him to improve relations with her mother, he had acquired a bottle of whisky, which he intended to give her purely for medicinal purposes.

Much to his chagrin, Mrs Tanner pounced on it. She said that as she was visiting her mother that very day, she would deliver it personally with his love. Constable Tanner painfully agreed.

Jack Tanner was on a loser from the start. Whatever the outcome of this dreadful state of affairs, he could not win. If he snatched the bottle back before she had a chance to sample it, what possible explanation could he give? If she actually tried a glass, his would be a fate worse than death!

Skidding to a halt at his mother-in-law's house, he

flung the back door open to be confronted by the worst possible situation. His wife's mother was at that precise moment lifting a glass of whisky to her lips.

"STOP!" He screeched, "Don't touch that, it's piddle!"

Constable Tanner's mother-in-law recoiled in horror. "You've done sum damn awful fings in yer time," she said, "but I 'ent never knowed a son-in-law that's got up ter the capers that you 'ave! I allus sed yer woz a wicked man, an' now I knows it! Me poor dear daughter's got a cross to bear an' no mistake. Git orf me property and don't ever darken me doorstep agin!"

With that she bundled him out of the door and slammed it behind him with a vengeance.

Constable Tanner's woes were twofold. He was in trouble with his wife. He explained lamely, that it was true that he had 'acquired' the bottle of whisky, he just hadn't said *where* he had acquired it. He told his wife that he had found it outside the *Five Bells*, which indeed could well have been true. He had subsequently discovered that it was a sample of holy water that belonged to Ern Packham, that was in transit to the Doctor in Orpington, being conveyed there by Ern's brother, Will.

Mrs Tanner tried very hard to pour oil on the troubled waters of her mother's relationship with Jack.

Even though his story was perfectly credible, the situation with his mother-in-law was such, that *any* incident concerning him, could be described as akin to lighting the blue touch paper and retiring immediately to a safe distance.

It was a year before normal relations were resumed between them. It is on record that she never accepted a drink from him again; *particularly* if it was offered in the public bar of the *Five Bells*!"

From that moment on, Constable Tanner would look askance at Grandad. He was never sure whether he had been set up by George Humble and Grandad. He even asked Grannie at the bus stop, in a wheedling way, how Grandad's brother, Ern, was getting on? He received a short answer. Grannie had heard of the nasty trick that he had played on his mother-in-law and said; "none the better for your askin'."

It was another contributory factor to the feud that existed between the Tanners and the Packhams, a feud that was to last for many years.

I am not sure of the outcome of Ern's urinary problems. Whatever happened, the events must have paled into insignificance compared to the trouble that his sample had caused.

CHAPTER SEVEN

Grace and Favour

It is fairly obvious in retrospect, that Grannie *almost* had a fling with Jimmy Trigwell, the signalman at Knockholt railway station.

Jimmy Trigwell and Grandad had been friends for many years. Jimmy lived in one of the railway cottages situated on Cadlocks Hill near to the site once occupied by Bowen's timber yard.

At that time, work on the railways was poorly paid. Jimmy had to resort to repairing shoes in order to make ends meet – at least that's what *he* said – the truth of the matter was that it provided a wonderful excuse, under the pretence of repairing shoes, to acquaint himself with any desirable ladies in the area. Grannie was one of the ladies on his list!

Earliest memories of Jimmy Trigwell, go back to the two couples – him and his wife, and Grannie and Grandad, all going to the Lewisham Hippodrome on a Saturday night. This was to experience the delights of cockles and whelks, and two hours of sitting in the gods, to see the latest London theatre extravaganza.

These were poor but happy days. The Trigwell's would spend Christmas days with us. The amazement, when Jimmy and Grandad gave an exhibition of banjo playing that took our breath away. They appeared, with their backs toward us, from behind the heavy curtains that shielded the pantry door. Suddenly, the most amazing sound of banjo playing came forth. We had never heard anything like it. Grandad and Jimmy suddenly spun round, and played music the like of which had never been heard in the old cottage before. Their fingers were a blur, their actions and synchronisation were perfect. They had their straw boaters on at rakish angles. Their music was magical. We sat with mouths wide open in amazement, it was a side of Grandad and Jimmy Trigwell that we had not known about.

That was until the gramophone record stuck! Grandad and Jimmy, who at the sight of our amazed expressions had great trouble keeping their faces straight, collapsed on chairs in peals of laughter, as the needle stuck in the groove and the gramophone repeated the same notes.

Jimmy seemed to visit us frequently. He spent many hours in the shed showing Grannie the noble art of snobbing; at least that was what he was supposed to be doing. We could never figure out what it was about repairing shoes that made Grannie's eyes sparkle. Whatever it was, it only seemed to happen on the days that Jimmy Trigwell gave Grannie cobbling lessons.

At this time, Grannie's only son, Wilfred, was an apprentice engine driver on Southern Railways. Grannie would walk across the fields to Knockholt Station in the afternoon, with sandwiches and a can of tea, ostensibly for her son to collect as he came through, on his way to Dunton Green, Brasted and Westerham. It was quite obvious that she could have prepared this in the morning before he left the house. The real reason for her visit was to see Jimmy Trigwell in the signal box.

Whilst this was undoubtedly only a mild flirtation, it probably added spice to Grannie's life. Grandad, although apparently never smelling a rat, rapidly took up shoe repairing. This obliviated the need for any shoe repairs, and the point of any future visits from the demon shoe repairer. Jimmy Trigwell turned his attentions to the *Five Bells* and pastures new. To the belle of the *Bells*, a delectable young lady named Grace King.

The alliance of Grace King and Albert Mills was the best known secret in Chelsfield. They both thought that the liaison was something known only to them. It was, in fact, known to the whole village.

It was common knowledge that at closing time, Grace would make a great show of bidding farewell to all and sundry, and particularly Albert, before putting on her bicycle clips, and disappearing into the night.

Everyone knew that her destination would be the large shed known as the Fire Station, situated in a field at the top end of the village. That it was known as a fire station was a misnomer, it contained a strange machine with four small cart wheels and a two-handed pump that was supposed to put fires out. To the best of my knowledge no one was designated as fireman. The only fire in the village – the one that burned down Mr Uhlrich's house, which was the nearest house to the fire station – did so because no one knew how to operate the fire engine. It was primarily, the large shed in which Mr Hogben kept the equipment with which he looked after the highways and byeways of Chelsfield village.

It did, however, have other uses.

The trouble started when Jimmy Trigwell looked for pastures new and found them in the Bunteresque form of Grace King.

Grace was not exactly a beauty. She had something – goodness knows what it was – but she definitely had something!

Her normal attire consisted of men's blue, pin-stripe trousers and bicycle clips. These did nothing to hide the violent-green socks and hob-nailed boots that were her trademark. A cardigan of sorts with holes at the elbows, was partially obscured by a waistcoat with most of the buttons missing. Surmounting all, was a navy-blue beret that fitted low over the eyes. This fitted tightly, which drew her eyes up, giving a perpetual look of surprise. Thick, horn-rimmed spectacles and a fringe completed a picture of rosy-cheeked humour that created devastation in the public bar of the *Five Bells*.

To say that the pending liaison between Grace and Jimmy caused problems to Albert would be an under-statement. When Jimmy and Grace played darts together, it was all that Albert could do to keep his eyes off them. You took your chance when ordering a drink at this time; Albert would pull the beer out of any pump whilst look-ing to see who was doing what to who on the dart board. Your change did not bear any resemblance to what it should to have been.

It became obvious that things were becoming serious when Jimmy would leave a shade before closing time. He would put on his bicycle clips, give his walrus mous-tache a twist, and with his cap set at a jaunty angle and a twinkle in his eye, pedal off into the night. Grace would disappear a few minutes later.

Albert would scream "TIME" at the top of his voice. He would move like a streak of light trying to wash the glasses, give the bar a sweep, and depart in hot pursuit of the other two.

He was never quick enough. By the time he reached the fire station, Jimmy would be pedalling smugly at top speed along the by-pass, on the way to his cottage on

Cadlocks Hill. Grace would be having problems with a headache.

One of the demon dart players at the *Bo-Peep* was a neighbour known as Terry Marr. He was not a particularly pleasant man. In fact he was renowned, not only for being the best darts player in the area, but also for deceiving any innocent visitor into playing darts with him. His ploy was always the same. Terry Marr would let the visitor win a game or two, and then suggest that to make things interesting, they play for a pint or two. He would then commence to win several games in devastating fashion, leaving his opponent gasping and taking several pints off him in the process.

The only person to ever beat Terry Marr consistently, was Grace King.

It was all to do with the local darts league. The *Bo-Peep* played the *Five Bells* and beat them hands down. Terry Marr was the man of the match. It was obvious that he soon had something going, apart from darts, with Grace King. It could not have been anything to do with looks; Terry Marr looked like Mr Punch, was ginger, and had blond eyelashes. He also rode a bicycle.

Albert and Jimmy Trigwell looked decidedly narked, when Terry Marr insisted on putting one arm around the ample girth of Grace, and held her dart hand with his dart hand, to show her the finer points of throwing darts.

They would have looked even more narked if they had known that after closing time, he had secret assignations with Grace, behind the avenue of trees at the church entrance. On these occasions she told both of the others that she had a splitting headache.

In the due course of time it could be said that Grace formed her own darts team. Jimmy Trigwell was a reasonable player and so was Albert, although he was somewhat restricted by the amount of time he was required to spend behind the bar. Terry Marr was the best player – providing he let Grace win the odd game or two, his position in the team was assured. It was 'Tinker' Thomas who completed the team.

'Tinker' Thomas worked for Stanley May, owner of the biggest farm in the area. 'Tinker's' job description could be that of 'bird scarer'. When times were good he stood in the cherry orchard opposite the *Bo-Peep* letting-fly with a twelve-bore to keep the birds away. When things were bad, his job was to discourage the birds by banging two saucepans together. Mostly it was a saucepan job.

Because the cherry orchard was next to the *Bo-Peep*, 'Tinker' Thomas had ample opportunity to practice on the dart board. He became a proficient darts player. He did, however, suffer many disadvantages; he had a menial occupation, and was left wanting in the cleanliness stakes. His one great advantage over his rivals, was that his cottage was up the lane by the avenue of trees that led to the church. He lived next to the object of his carnal desires.

His cottage was next to a farm appropriately named Julian Brimstone. 'Tinker' Thomas was not averse, on cold, rainy nights, to giving Grace a lift home on the crossbar of his bicycle. He would give her a lift back the next day so that she could collect her own bicycle. This caused problems amongst the others. Albert, denied his pleasures would go home in a white fury – Jimmy would actually get home early, and Terry Marr would sulk behind a newspaper for the rest of the evening. Credit must be given to Grace. She could not refuse 'Tinker' his kind offer, and keeping the others on the ball did no harm at all.

Plate 1: Squire Warings House, Woodlands *(where Grandad was head butler)*

Plate 2: A typical scene of women land-workers at the end of the day

Plate 3: Knockholt railway station 1880. Where all brass was polished, flowers grew on platforms, and real fires burned in waiting rooms

Plate 4: The Five Bells *at Chelsfield: where Bert Parks reigned supreme*

Plate 5: Open-topped 407 bus at the Five Bells *(Circa 1932). This later became the 477 route to Orpington and Dartford*

Plate 6: The Kent Hounds *once stood on Back Hill, the only main road in the area. Originally a drapery shop that sold ale*

Plate 7: Alwens shop. A general store situated on Well Hill; where Grannie broke the sound barrier on her way to Chelsfield, on a bicycle made for her by Grandad

Plate 8: Grandad and Grannie Packham with daughter Dorrie in 1900. Taken at their first marital home, in one of the cottages in Hollybush Lane

*Plate 9: A photograph (incorrectly imposed), of the house of old
Mr Uhlrich, previously situated on the site occupied by Bert Parks' house*

*Plate 10: A forced landing (Circa 1912) between Well Hill and Skeet Hill.
Grandad had a souvenir of this in a cupboard by the fireplace*

Plate 11: Aunt Eliza Martin, Grandad's sister who lived at Bucks Cross. Grandad's brother Ern lodged with her on occasions. They fought like cat and dog

Plate 12: Grandad's brother Ern, with one of Grandad's 'Lion' bicycles

Plate 13: Little Nell in the garden of Yewtree House *(Circa 1918)*

It was obvious, however, that such a tenuous arrangement could not last for ever; the best laid schemes of mice and men must come to an end, and come to an end they did. Strangely, all because of a puncture. Rather like the gunfight at the OK Corral, all four, unknown to the others, decided to hide behind the fire station on the same night. The problems were compounded when Grace had a flat tyre and arrived late. In the inky-black darkness, Jimmy Trigwell leaped on a dark shape that he assumed to be Grace, and commenced to caress 'Tinker' Thomas. 'Tinker' thinking that his luck had changed gave Jimmy a kiss; he suspected that all was not well when he had trouble with Jimmy's walrus moustache. In the meantime, Albert and Terry Marr were engaged in a similar exercise; Albert received a sharp stab in the chest from the darts in Terry's top pocket.

"I'm 'avin' trouble wiv yer brooch, darlin'," he crooned, as he passionately ran his hands all over Terry's chest. Authenticity was added to the proceedings by Grace, squeaking with delight at having so many hands to deal with.

"Christ!" said 'Tinker' to Jimmy in the darkness. "You 'ent bloody Grace!"

Jimmy, slowly realising the horror of the situation and wiping his mouth frantically on his coat sleeve spluttered, "I've just given yer a bloody kiss!"

Terry Marr shouted at Albert, "Git's yer 'and out from under me weskit!"

A confused Albert shouted back "wot yer wearin' a brooch fer?"

It was all very confusing.

That night, four disgruntled old boys pedalled home their separate ways. Apart from the shout-up, the matter was never mentioned again. The darts team disbanded.

Things were never the same. An odd atmosphere seemed to pervade the air whenever they met. Grace never bothered to repair her puncture. She abandoned her bicycle and either walked, or was carried triumphantly about on 'Tinker's' crossbar. He considered himself the victor in the grace and favour competition.

He should have watched Albert a little more carefully. On the occasions that Grace walked to the *Five Bells*, she had of necessity to walk home afterwards. On these occasions he would have noticed that Albert was not far behind. And should he have discreetly followed Albert, he would have heard a certain amount of scuffling from behind the fire station.

Enough, in fact, to take the smug look of satisfaction off the face of 'Tinker' Thomas!

CHAPTER EIGHT

A Stick in Time

It was all to do with bicycles. In an age when everybody walked, the bicycle was the most desirable possession. Very few people owned motor-cycles. A car was beyond the reach of all except the wealthiest.

The average bicycle, as ridden by Grace and her friends, was an upright affair, probably second-hand, and had been hand-painted many times with whatever paint happened to be handy. No one that I knew had ever owned a new one. That was until Syd Forman became the envy of the area; he bought himself a brand-new racing machine.

Bob Hogben almost choked. A new bicycle was bad enough, but a *brand-new racing machine* was almost too much to bear.

Needless to say, Syd Forman rubbed it well in. He developed an unbearably supercilious air whenever he passed by. He even pretended that he was changing gear with a non-existent three-speed gear. He accomplished this by flicking his pedals back and forth as he cycled along. The fact that he passed by twice each day, repeating his gear-changing act every time, predetermined an event that was bound to happen.

Syd Forman was a gardener of repute. So was Mr Gregory. Mr Gregory lived on the opposite side of the lane to Bob's house. Apart from his gardening prowess, he was an extremely ill-tempered man. He and Mr Hogben, Bob's father, regularly had awful rows about the unruly Hogben children throwing balls into his garden.

On the day in question, not having a bike, Bob Hogben had been playing with the next best thing; a hoop made from an old bicycle wheel with no spokes. He had asked his father to buy him a bicycle for Christmas and received a cuff round the ear instead. He was not happy; he felt that the world had dealt him a bad hand. He sat on the bank by the side of the road, disconsolately toying with the short stick that he had been using to propel his hoop.

Mr Gregory and Syd Forman were arch enemies. It was all because they grew prize marrows and competed against one another at the village fête. Syd Forman consistently grew bigger marrows than Mr Gregory. That was the problem – he regularly walked off with first prize in this event.

After four wins in succession, Mr Gregory called Syd Forman a cheat. He said that he was using certain substances not allowed. He shouted, "I'm buggered if I 'ent a'goin' to beat yer bloody fair an' square! You see if I don't!"

Mr Gregory sowed fifty marrow seeds. He selected the best seedling and nurtured it every hour of the day. He watched the weather forecast and either covered it or uncovered it. He tucked it in every night. It had the best possible soil and the best feed that money could buy. When it came to the actual position in the garden, this was calculated to the inch. The site chosen was in a sheltered position, next to the hedge that bordered the lane. That was to be its undoing!

In the due course of time, Mr Gregory's marrow began

to grow. To say that it was a monster would be an understatement. People came from far and wide to gaze in awe at its size. Three weeks' before the village fête it was measured. It was three feet and six inches long, with a girth of fifty inches. Mr Gregory viewed it with pride. No one was allowed near it.

Syd Forman spied on Mr Gregory's marrow every day he passed. From his bicycle he was afforded a grandstand view over the hedge. He knew that Mr Gregory had the better of him this time. He would have resorted to any lengths in order to win the village fête. In fact, he did.

But not in the way that one would have imagined. . . . Strange things can be attributed to the cause of accidents. The obscure reasons for their cause can be even more peculiar. In this case, the intense irritation caused by the supercilious look on Syd Forman's face as he pretended to change gear, was the obscure reason. The cause was the stick that Bob Hogben was playing with.

This was only a twig really. It can have been no more than half an inch thick and certainly no more than eight inches long. The problem that it caused had to be seen to be believed.

For no reason, other than perhaps for his father's refusal to buy him a bike for Christmas, Bob tossed the stick with irritation, in the general direction of Syd Forman. What happened next defies description.

The stick described a near-perfect arc. It actually managed to get between the spokes of the front wheel, behind the front forks!

In the space of one second, Syd's racing bicycle stopped dead. There was a brief period of awful noise, as his impetus tore several spokes from the front wheel. It was what happened next that really caused the trouble.

Syd literally took off! With an awful scream he described almost the same arc that the stick had, except that he completely vanished over the hedge into Mr Gregory's garden.

Mr Gregory heard the scream, and leaping up from studying a gardening formula for an even better marrow fertiliser, was aghast to see Syd Forman, actually up to his knees in the middle of his beloved prize marrow!

It was a normal procedure for Mr Gregory to rush out shouting when Mr Hogben's kids threw balls into his garden. This was different. He was raging like a bull! Poor Syd Forman stood transfixed in terror. Mr Gregory had by now ripped off his jacket and rolled up his sleeves. He was squaring up like an old time boxer.

"Yer bloody cheat!" he roared, "First, I'm a'goin' ter give yer a bloody good hidin' an' then I'm a'goin' ter finish off the job yer started on me marrer, only I'm a'goin' ter use yer bloody 'ead ter do it wiv!"

Terror gave Syd Forman strength. With a supreme effort he managed to free his feet. Leaping the hedge into the lane, he met Mr Hogben, who, assuming that his children had caused the trouble, was rushing – as he normally did – to do battle with Mr Gregory. He flung his cap on the ground.

Mr Gregory and Mr Hogben met in the lane. Syd Forman, covered in marrow, stood with his wrecked bicycle in the middle. The scene was not good

Within seconds, Mr Hogben and Mr Gregory, like a pair of fighting cocks, were circling around, thumbing their noses as boxers do, thrashing the air into a frenzy with poor Syd in the middle.

Syd kept ducking as blows hummed over his head. "Wot the 'ell's goin' on!" he yelped. "I 'ent done nuffink!"

"It might be nuffink ter you" snarled Mr Gregory, "but that's me prize bloody marrer you squashed flat! I'm a'goin' to knock yer bloody block off!"

Syd was in a spot. Mr Gregory was in front with flailing fists; all hell and damnation. Mr Hogben behind, hopping about like a Jack-in-the-box, doing his impression of a windmill.

Looking at Mr Hogben, Syd said, "Wot are yer bloody fightin' me fer?"

Mr Hogben replied, "I 'ent a'fightin' you. It's 'im I'm arter! You're jest in the bloody way!"

"Wot are yer fightin' 'im fer?" asked Syd.

"Any one as takes on me kids, takes on me as well!" Said Bill Hogben, eyes blazing.

"There 'ent no bloody kids!" said Syd Forman in bewilderment.

Bob, aware that his well-lobbed stick had caused a major incident, and knowing that his father would more than likely whack his pants until the dust flew, had decided that discretion was the better part of valour and disappeared behind the hedge.

Mr Hogben stopped flailing. "Whose he bloody well chasing, then?" he said, glaring at Mr Gregory.

"Me!" screamed Syd.

Mr Hogben looked quizzical. "You throwed a ball in 'is garden, then?" he asked.

"No!" said Syd, "I trod on 'is marrer!"

"Trod on it!" roared Mr Gregory, "Yer bloody well jumped all over it!" And once again he began squaring up to Syd.

"I'd leave 'im to it if I was you," said Bill Hogben, and picking up Syd's bike, helped him on his way.

Admittedly, the front wheel was now oval, and Syd's progress was reminiscent of riding a horse, but Mr Hogben's action had stopped trouble and saved a major incident.

All in all, the outcome was very satisfactory. Bob had removed Syd Forman's supercilious look. In the general furore, everyone had forgotten that it was Bob's stick that had caused the problem. Syd's bike was out of commission for several weeks. His marrow won the competition in the village fête. Mr Hogben had defended his children with his life, and Mr Gregory felt that he had showed Syd Forman and Bill Hogben a thing or two. It all came right in the end!

CHAPTER NINE

A Licensing Dynasty

It seemed that Bert Parks had always been landlord of the *Five Bells* in Chelsfield. He had, at an earlier time, worked at the Woolwich Arsenal. As far as this story is concerned, however, he was the landlord of the pub in question, and the uncrowned mayor of the village.

Apart from being an impressive figure, his origins as a publican were the *Anchor and Hope* in Orpington and the *Rock and Fountain* at Well Hill. Bert had many irons in the fire. He could be classed as an opportunist.

While he was landlord at the *Rock and Fountain* he ventured into other enterprises; that of the manufacture of radio receivers, and the business of pig farming.

When radio became popular, a large club-room at the rear of the pub became a manufacturing workshop.

As he regularly donated a prize of a piglet to the village fête, a sow was installed on a patch of land at the back of the pub with this in mind. A problem arose, however. A boar is necessary to assist a sow in the production of a piglet, and so is an ample supply of swill.

An elderly gentleman named 'Chicken' Smith (who was Albert Blott's father-in-law and lived with Albert and his wife in Maple House) ran a few chickens on a patch of land next to the *Rock and Fountain*. His name came about because there were several Smiths in the village: he was called 'Chicken' to differentiate him from the others. Old Mr Smith also owned a young boar which he kept on a patch of land next to Albert Blott's place.

'Chicken' Smith was something out of *Old Moore's Almanac*. He was old, bent, and gnarled, with a huge, white beard. He sported a battered, oil-stained straw hat; gaiters and hob-nailed boots completed a picture of a man of the soil, who had spent his entire life toiling in the fields. He pushed a wheel-barrow that must have weighed three hundred-weight.

It was part of life, to see 'Chicken' Smith pushing his enormous barrow, twice daily along the half-mile stretch from Albert Blott's place to his patch at Well Hill. Not only was it possible to *see* him on his daily drudge, but with his heavy hob-nailed boots and the iron-shod cart-wheel grinding on the uneven flint road, it was quite possible to hear him coming from Albert's house a quarter of a mile away.

It was the cost of having to buy a piglet from old Joey Turner in the village each year that made Bert Parks go into the pig business. It was the sight of 'Chicken' Smith heaving his barrow up Well Hill that brought out his opportunism. He put two and two together and made four; old-man Smith and his boar, and Bert and his sow. He devised a way to cut out old Joey and the price of his piglets, and to do something about the cost of the swill that Joey was making him pay!

Bert Parks arranged to be near the door of the four-ale bar of the *Rock and Fountain* as 'Chicken' Smith, purple in the face and fighting a losing battle, was struggling to get his wheel-barrow up the hill.

"Rest your ol' feet," crooned the artful Bert, "Come on in and 'ave a pint on me!"

'Chicken' Smith could not believe his ears. To be

asked to take a rest and have a free pint in to the bargain, was too good an opportunity to miss. He fell into the bar, flopped in the nearest seat, and accepted the pint with relish.

It was after the second pint, when Bert had lulled the old man into a sense of false security, that he sprung the trap.

"I've bin thinkin'," said Bert in a wily manner, "of a way ter make yer life easier, and make yersel' a few bob as well!"

"Ow's that, then?" said the unsuspecting 'Chicken' Smith.

Bert went right in at the deep end. "Bring yer boar up ter my sow," he said. "Let 'em 'ave a weddin' night, and any piglets she has above three, yer can 'ave!"

'Chicken' Smith's brain methodically worked out that it could be expected that the average litter was in the order of six or seven. Despite knowing Bert's wily reputation, the beer caused him to throw all caution to the wind. "Done!" he said. From that moment, the die was cast.

It was later that day, when 'Chicken' Smith was having his evening meal with Albert Blott and his wife, that he mentioned the deal that he had struck with Bert Parks. There was a clatter as Albert dropped his knife and fork in horror.

"How the bleedin' 'ell are yer a'goin' ter git the boar up ter Well Hill?" he said. "If yer walk 'im all that way, he'll be knackered afore 'ee starts, it'll be a funeral he'll be a'goin' to, not 'is bloody weddin'!"

"I've worked it out," said the old man thoughtfully, "'ee 'ent goin' ter walk, 'ee can go in style in the barrer."

"And 'ow the 'ell are yer goin' ter git 'im in the barrer?" said Albert.

"We three are a'goin' ter give 'im a lift up!" said the old man looking at Albert as if he were the village idiot.

And so it was, that at seven o'clock the next morning, 'Chicken' Smith, a bad-tempered Albert, and an even worse tempered Mrs Blott, set about the task of getting old 'Chicken' Smith's pet boar – Cecil by name – into the wheel barrow.

The weather was bad on that particular morning, a howling gale in fact. Staggering about in Wellington boots and Sou'westers with a reluctant boar, did not do a lot for Albert and his wife. As 'Chicken' Smith said "they 'ad a bloody good row about it!" This culminated in Mrs Blott falling in the mud and saying "bugger the bloody pig!" and storming off indoors.

After an hour fraught with problems, old Mr Smith finally went on his way with Cecil loaded on the barrow. He was up to his neck in a hop-sack, and not looking too pleased about it. Three hundred-weight of wheel-barrow was bad enough, but when loaded with the best part of one and a half hundred-weight of struggling pig whose sole intention seemed to be to get out, was well nigh impossible.

To say that 'Chicken' Smith was breathing heavily when he came passed our house would be an understatement. He was purple in the face and staggering all over the road. Sparks were emanating from the iron-shod wheel as Cecil fought to get out. The noise he made was deafening.

Grandad, alerted by the racket, peered out from behind the curtains to investigate and said with amazement, "Wot the 'ell's 'ee on about! I reckon 'ee'd git on better if 'ee sat in the bloody barrer and let Cecil do the pushin'."

Finally, in a near state of collapse, and with help from

Bert, the last few yards of Well Hill were negotiated and Cecil was confronted with his bride.

It was at this point that a conference was held between Bert and an exhausted Mr Smith. There seemed to be a problem as to how they would know that the marriage had been consummated. "I can't stand and watch 'em all bloody day," said Bert, "I've got a pub ter run."

It was then that 'Chicken' had a rush of blood to the head. "I reckon," he said thoughtfully, "that we ort ter do as they does when they puts the ram ter the sheep."

"Wot's that, then?" said Bert.

"Puts a dob of paint on 'is belly," said 'Chicken', "and when she gits a bit coloured on the back, then we know's he's done the trick!"

So without further ado. Bert appeared with an old tin of paint from his shed, and commenced to give Cecil a coat of paint.

The fact that it was the same brilliant blue with which he had been decorating the pub lavatory, appeared to cause some problems.

His sow took one look at Cecil in his highly decorated, blue wedding suit from the confines of her sty, and refused to come out.

In fact she set about him whenever he poked his nose into the bridal suite.

After several hours of watching through knot-holes in the shed, it was decided by Bert and Mr Smith, that there was not going to be a love match. With a struggle similar to that which had taken place in the morning, Cecil was reinstated in the hop-sack and loaded on the barrow. Old-man Smith stopped at our cottage and consulted Grandad.

"I a'knows 'ee 'ent good lookin," said Mr Smith, "but she 'ent no bloody oil-paintin' neither!"

CHAPTER NINE

"Maybe that's the trouble," said Grandad. "Could be, she's a bit bloody pertikler about the colour of 'is weddin' suit. I'd give 'im another go tomorrer if I was you."

The next morning, Albert Blott, who had to feed the chickens and collect the eggs at an early hour, appeared when Mrs Blott called him in for breakfast. All three sat down in silence. Mrs Blott was dreading the call to get Cecil on the barrow. 'Chicken' Smith was not looking forward to it either! It was Albert that broke the glad tidings. "Don't know wot you two are lookin' so bloody glum about?" he said (knowing full well the reason for their misery). "If yer care ter look up the yard, you'll see a sight fer sore eyes. Cecil's up there as perky as ninepence, sittin' in the bloody barrer waitin' fer yet to shove 'im up Well Hill!"

It was glad news indeed. Without further ado, old-man Smith, with much heaving and shoving, wheeled Cecil up to his reluctant bride on Well Hill. Fresh paint was liberally applied by Bert, and the courting couple left to their own devices.

Sadly, Bert's sow was extremely difficult. Either Cecil was ugly, or she did not care for his choice of colour. Problems arose when the time came to go home. 'Chicken' Smith tried to get him in the barrow but Cecil had the bit between his teeth and refused to go. Evidently, he realised that there was more to life than swill. It took two hours of sweating and fuming to get him aboard.

The next morning, once again Cecil was already in the barrow. Old-man Smith for the third time sweated his way up Well Hill, but this time things were different. Bert was sure it was the colour that had put the blushing bride off and this time tried an old tin of bright yellow that he had repainted an old bicycle with. It worked like magic. Bert's sow, panting with desire, chased Cecil all over the yard. In the evening, as old-man Smith said, "Cecil was bloody pleased ter git on the barrer an' come 'ome!"

Bert Parks knew that the job was well done, when he looked out of the pub window and saw his sow – apparently wearing a floral dress – happily frolicking in the yard. It was mostly brilliant-green, flecked with bright-yellow. The consummated bride, from that moment on, answered to the name of Emerald!

CHAPTER TEN

Business Matters

'Chicken' Smith, happy at a job well done, sat back and waited for a bunch of porkers to drop in his lap. Admittedly, it had been hard work shoving Cecil up and down Well Hill, but all he had to do now, was to sit back, and, in due course, become a pig farmer.

Bert Parks, however, was engaged in other business matters. He had the reputation of being an opportunist. The course of events proved the point.

Mr Smallwood, the village baker, had intimated to Bert that he was having problems disposing of stale bread. Although Mr Smallwood used his excess stock to make the most magnificent bread puddings, he was constantly fighting a losing battle against an ever-increasing pile of stale bread. It had got to the stage when it was occupying valuable storage space that was urgently needed for other things. He happened to mention that he would even pay to have it removed. With a gleam in his eye, Bert said that for a small sum, paid on a regular basis, he could probably arrange to have it shifted; he mentioned five shillings a week. Mr Smallwood jumped at the idea. A deal was struck.

Old Joey Turner, who lived in the Ivy cottages near to the centre of the village, kept a pig or two on a plot of land behind the old cricket pavilion. Both he and his son were the proud owners of a high-speed horse and cart. Horses and carts came in several sizes. By todays standards, industrial ones could be classed as Leyland lorries and the norm would be Ford Cortinas. On such a scale, Joe Turner's would be a top of the range, grand prix Ferrari! It was small, robustly built, and was the only cart in the area fitted with actual car tyres. Whether it was the tyres that gave young Joe the speed bug I do not know. What I do know is, that he regularly came through Chelsfield village like a bat out of hell. Other horse-drawn carts plodded everywhere in leisurely fashion, but not young Joey Turner. As Grandad delicately put it, "'ee's goin' so bloody fast, like as not 'e'll pass the bloody 'orse!"

There was, however, a reason for young Joey's swiftness. Bert Parks had taken him on one side and put a proposition to him. "Look here young Joe," he said with a knowledgeable air. "I've come to an arrangement with Mr Smallwood that's goin' ter cost me money. Fer a price, I'm goin' ter take all 'is stale bread orf 'is 'ands, and if you likes ter take it up ter me sow at Well Hill, any piglets that the old sow has over three, I'll give yer!"

Young Joe, like 'Chicken' Smith, knew the capability of a sow of the calibre of Emerald to produce multiple births. Like 'Chicken' Smith, he too could spot a bargain. He could see himself on the way to becoming a pig farmer.

"Done!" he said with relish.

Bert tapped the side of his nose and said, "This 'ere's between you an' me. Old 'Chicken' Smith's arter a few piglets, but they're yours if yer feeds the old gal, so keep it ter yersel."

Young Joey nodded and kept Bert's secret. He felt that

his association with the landlord of the *Rock and Foun -
tain* was the first step on the road to success.

And so, every afternoon at about four o'clock, young
Joey Turner could be seen flying past our house – with a
load of last weeks' bread from Mr Smallwood – on his
way to the abode of a plump young lady who lived on
Well Hill who answered to the name of Emerald.

Although the Turner family lived in the old Ivy cottages at the centre of the village, they considered themselves to be socially superior to their neighbours. They
would emphasise that they lived in 'Crosshall' Cottages
and not 'Ivy' Cottages. The fact that it was all the same
row was irrelevant; they classed themselves with the
'Crosshall' end, and not the menial occupants of the rest
of the terrace. It was all to do with the fact that Joey and
his father were self-employed, independent traders. In
todays jargon they would be known as wheeler-dealers.
Mrs Turner sold greengrocery from her cottage. Joe and
his father supplied the produce. They also dealt in logs,
pig swill, pigs, holly and mistletoe at Christmas, and
anything else that needed shifting from one place to
another.

It will be seen, that with all these sidelines, and a burning ambition to get on, young Joe had to move swiftly to
get them all in.

Confusion always reigned because of the custom at
that time, of naming sons after their fathers. In my own
case, my fathers name was James. My second name was
James, and so we became big Jim and little Jim. This was
all very well, but when I grew up and became larger than
my father, this caused problems. A reference to 'big
Jim', which originally had meant my father was now a
reference to me. This resulted in questions as to who
they were really referring to. It was all very confusing. It

wasted many hours of my life. It was the same with old Joey Turner and young Joey Turner and old Bert Parks and his son young Bert Parks. Bert Parks also had a son who he christened Douglas. You would have thought that Douglas would have learned from his father's mistake – he had a son who he promptly named Douglas. Any reference to the Parks family, was always followed by a lengthy enquiry – was the one being discussed either old Bert or young Bert? Or old Doug or young Doug? The fact that they were all publicans added to the confusion!

This confusion manifested itself in a very strange way. At the time of Dunkirk (the place where the German armies had driven the allied forces into the sea during World War II), old Doug Parks (who was in the middle of it all), had not been heard of for many weeks. Bert and his wife were worried sick.

Doug, in the chaos at Dover, found himself with thousands of other troops, packed in a train with locked doors, and bound for London.

It was not long before he noticed that the train was passing through Sevenoaks and Dunton Green. Although not stopping, it slowed down – almost to walking pace, at Orpington station.

Doug managed to get a window open, and shouted at a porter standing on the platform. "Tell Bert Parks at the *Anchor and Hope* that I'm all right!"

This caused some confusion. The railway staff held a meeting. They all agreed that Bert Parks was the landlord of the *Five Bells* at Chelsfield. It was obvious that someone who was bomb-happy was in a confused state. It might even have been meant for a customer at the *Anchor and Hope* that no one knew. It was a passing passenger who remarked that the landlord of the *Anchor and Hope* was a Bert Parks who was the son of the Bert Parks at the *Five Bells*. That explained everything – a quick telephone call to Bert Parks at the pub in Orpington resulted in an equally quick telephone call to Mr and Mrs Parks at the *Five Bells* at Chelsfield. The glad tidings that their son was safe called for free drinks all round. The celebrations lasted all day.

And so the scene was set. Bert's sow, Emerald, was well and truly in the family way, having been put there by the efforts of 'Chicken' Smith and his boar, Cecil. Mr Small-wood was paying Bert Parks dearly for the removal of his excess bread. Joey Turner was collecting this bread daily, and shipping it up to Bert's shed at the *Rock and Fountain* on Well Hill. Bert had promised both 'Chicken' Smith and Joe Turner that they would get any piglets from the litter after the first three. An impossible situation. But was it? What neither 'Chicken' Smith, or Joey Turner knew, was the actual date that Emerald was due to make Cecil a father.

Joey flew back and forth, old Mr Smith called in for a drink every day, and asked whether Emerald had far-rowed and when the great event was due? Bert said "Buggered if I know!" And left it at that.

Finally, he could postpone it no longer. Bert broke the awful news separately to 'Chicken' Smith and Joey Turner.

"An event has occurred that is unknown in the annals of pig breeding," he said. "It's a complete puzzle as to 'ow 'it as 'appened, but Emerald has given birth to a lit-ter of only three piglets."

He told 'Chicken' Smith that he put it down to "too much bumpin' about in the barrer." Young Joey Turner was told that it was "too much bloody bread." He felt "very sad for them, particularly in view of all their efforts, but a bargain was a bargain, and he *had* said that he would only give them any piglets after the first three, so regretfully they would have to put it down to luck and hope for better next time." He went gleefully on his way.

'Chicken' Smith was not happy. In spite of Cecil regularly getting in the barrow, he was put on short rations and left sitting there. Joey Turner was even worse, he had not only burned out both front wheel-bearings on his cart, but the brake blocks as well! Now that Joey had cleared out Mr Smallwood's stale bread, Bert Parks cancelled the contract for its removal.

The only one who came out of this smelling of roses was Bert Parks. It was he, that in the still of a Sunday afternoon, silently delivered five piglets to a place in Chelsfield Lane known as George's Pig Farm. He received a wad of notes in return. It was this that made Bert Parks an opportunist!

Another specialist in the business of the horse-drawn conveyance (in this case the pony and trap), was a character who answered to the name of Arthur Checksfield.

No one was ever sure whether Arthur Checksfield actually earned a living selling vegetables or not. Everyone grew their own and people would avoid him like the plague because of his awful stutter.

However, Arthur could be seen at any time of the day, meandering along without a care in the world, with an ancient donkey and trap that had been sold to him by the infamous Tommy Lee.

The truth of the matter was, that Tommy Lee's donkey was on his last legs and was bound for the knackers yard. Tommy had persuaded Arthur that there would be rich pickings to be had for anyone with the initiative to start a vegetable round. He convinced Arthur that he was just the chap for the job.

In the time that Arthur Checksfield stood – making chuffing noises for ten minutes – without a word coming out, Tommy Lee had quoted him a price, knocked it down for cash, spit on his hand, and clinched the deal. Arthur Checksfield stood with mouth agape. Tommy helped himself to five pounds from Arthur's jacket pocket, and Arthur Checksfield found himself the proud owner of an ailing donkey on it's last legs, and a trap that had been used for carting everything from dead sheep to horse manure. Hardly a vehicle from which an aspiring entrepreneur should conduct the sale of fresh garden produce!

Arthur Checksfield was a regular caller at the old cottage. Grannie would buy something from him out of the goodness of her heart. Bryan and I would always keep out of the way when he called. A deaf Grannie, and stuttering Arthur making chuffing noises like a two-stroke motor cycle, would be embarrassing in the extreme. We thought it dreadful that Grannie could treat him the way that she did. She would ask him how much his broad beans were, and then go and feed the dog whilst he stood chuffing for five minutes. She always seemed to arrive back as he blurted out "Ter-ter-ter-tuppence a pound!"

"Tuppence a pound!" she would exclaim. "I 'ent payin' that! How much are yer onions?"

Arthur would wind himself up to blurt out another sentence – Grannie would go and fill the kettle. She would come back just as Arthur ejaculated, "Ter-ter-ter-tuppence a pound!" (Everything seemed to be tuppence a pound – it was probably the easiest price for him to stutter.) Grannie would agree to this, take the onions, and ask him for a packet of 'Dinky' curlers (these were evil, little hair-curlers made of corrugated tin, specially designed to draw blood). Grannie used these to "put's me 'air up at night." Why she regularly asked Arthur Checksfield for 'Dinky' curlers, no one knows, to the best of our knowledge he only ever sold vegetables. We felt that Grannie was being kind because no one else would talk to him.

There would always be an awful row when Grandad saw what Grannie had bought from Mr Checksfield. "Wot the bloody 'ell 'ave yer got apples fer?" Grandad would shout. "Christ, woman! We've got three bloody orchards of 'em out there. I can't get rid of the damn things, an' there yer are, a'buyin' on 'em! You must be out of yer 'ead! I'll tell yer summink else, don't ask me ter eat the bloody things, they're covered in sheep's poop! Bloody top me, I kin see yer face if I bought a bushel in 'ere covered in that lot. I'd soon be bloody well told wot ter do wiv 'em!"

Arthur Checksfield was one of the many horse and cart traders that called at our door. All the delivery men had horses and carts, every farm vehicle was a cart. They were wonderful things to hang on to for mile after mile of free rides. They were massive, with huge brake blocks operated by a handle four feet long. Dangling chains suspended great iron shoes from which sparks flew. They were slipped under the iron-shod wheels when the brake blocks could no longer hold them. The wooden wheel-hubs always seemed to contain vast amounts of grease. They were large and slow-moving enough to jump and walk on, just for the hell of it!

The Norstead Manor Dairy, the Co-op from St Mary Cray, Mr Smallwood the baker, Stiggers, the paraffin man from Dunton Green, Charlie Strout the butcher, all had horses and carts – motor cars were yet to come.

The very first delivery vehicle to appear at Maypole was an orange 'Trojan' van with the words *Libby's Tea* on the side. It was shaped like an inverted flat-iron with wheels like orange dustbin lids. It made the most awful whirring sound and was driven by a massive, fully-exposed chain to the back wheels. This was perpetually slack and hung almost to the ground. It frightened Grannie to death. She scuttled into the pantry whenever it passed, and would only come out when it had gone.

The 'Trojan' did not frighten her half as much as a visit from the coalman. When the time came for him to abandon his horse and cart, he purchased the most awful contraption. It was a steam-lorry. The front-end had the appearance of a London tram. It had double solid tyres, a high chimney behind the cab that belched steam and smoke, and a raging furnace in the fire-box below. The appearance was awesome, it shook the ground like thunder, belched fire and sparks – it seemed incapable of stopping. The coalman would deliver his load at high speed while the thing was still moving. It seemed that half-a-ton of coal would be unloaded and paid for in ten seconds.

The time of the horse and cart was passing. The times were changing.

CHAPTER ELEVEN

Trouser Trouble

Part of life at the old cottage were the five Rhode Island hens and a Golden Cuckoo-Maran cockerel, that constantly hung about the back doorway. They were all that remained of a once prosperous chicken farm; one of the many business ventures that Grandad had started, but lost interest in.

The Maran cockerel answered to the name of 'Trousers'. This came about because of a sequence of events in which Grannie was involved. Originally the cockerel had been purchased by Grandad, to revive his flagging interest in chicken farming. 'Trousers' was a championship bird who, Grandad hoped, by crossing with his Rhode-Island Red hens, would produce a large table bird, prolific in the production of the darkest brown eggs in Kent.

At the time of his purchase, he was known as 'Prince William the Fourth of Holbeck' – at least that was the name on his certificate of pedigree. I suspect, however, that as Grandad had bought him from Tommy Lee, a wily old traveller, who on many occasions in the past had got the better of Grandad in various business transactions, that the certificate gave the distinct impression of being hand-written by Tommy.

Grandad would have none of this. Even though the offspring all laid normal-coloured eggs, and turned out either North-Holland Blues or Rhode-Island Reds. Grandad would not accept that once again Tommy Lee had got the better of him. He lost interest and the chickens became family pets.

There was a strong attachment between Grannie and 'Trousers'. It went back to the time when he was seen standing on one leg, holding the other up in a contorted fashion as if it pain. Grannie caught him, and on examination, it was found that he had trodden on a screw which had penetrated the length of his leg. All that was visible was the screw-head on the pad of his foot.

Grannie and Grandad went into conference. "'Ow the 'ell am I a'goin' ter git the bloody thing out?" said Grandad in a state of panic.

Grannie, sitting by the fire (with the cockerel standing in a bowl of hot water laced with disinfectant on her lap), replied with the utmost simplicity, "with a pair of pliers I 'spects!"

"Christ!" said Grandad, getting hold of the wrong end of the stick, "I'm buggered if you 'ent a bloody cannibal! Fancy pullin' 'is bloody foot orf with the pliers, wot possesses yer, woman! 'Ent yer got no feelin's?"

Grannie, ignoring Grandad's mistake, and ever the essence of practicability said, "Well, 'ent yer got a screwdriver, then?"

Grandad blinked and said, "Wot fer?"

Grannie replied, "That's wot unscrews screws, 'ent it?"

A screwdriver was dutifully produced, and Grandad, cap on backwards and up to the neck in a white sheet, proceeded to operate.

Dorrie and Little Nell, Grannie and Grandad's daughters, provided assistance. Dorrie mopped Grandad's perspiring brow, Little Nell cleaned his spectacles when they misted up. It was a repetition of when Grandad's rat trap had chopped the cats leg off. The only difference was that 'Jumbo' had been out for the count, 'Trousers' was very much wide awake. The odd thing was that no anaesthetic seemed to be needed. Grannie held a handful of corn in her free hand, and 'Trousers' never stopped eating.

The whole operation went remarkably smoothly. Grandad gently engaged the screw with the screwdriver and carefully unscrewed one-and-a-half inches of it. Apart from a dob of Snowfire Cream (which Grannie used for chilblains), and a sticking plaster to keep the dirt out, 'Trousers' seemed none the worse for his experience.

Sadly, things did not turn out too good. Slowly 'Trousers' began to lose the use of his legs. It was the hens that now did the chasing. Things were very different – they knocked the stuffing out of him for a change. He was no longer Cock of the Walk.

Grannie retrieved him from a fate worse than death. Although Ern said that "'ee was only fit fer the stew pot, 'ee weren't no good fer nothin'!" Grannie, on a point of principle (the point being that she was going to prove Ernie wrong), was determined that she was going to nurse him back to health.

Within a short while she had made a sling-like arrangement in which the invalid was suspended by a long cord. It was hung from an apple tree which grew by the back door. He was positioned so that his crippled feet just touched the ground. Grannie fed him constantly on the fat of the land. Apart from his legs, he seemed to go from strength to strength.

There was, however, one problem. Grannie had used a

sacking material to make the sling. It was harsh and abrasive. After a short period it began to wear the feathers off the underside of his nether regions. He began to go bald in the most embarrassing places.

Grandad examined things. "No doubt about it, Ellie," he said, "You can't be a'leavin' 'im 'angin' thataways, with all them damn feathers gorn an' winter a'comin', he'll catch his bloody death!" Grannie walked about with a worried look on her face biting her lip. Drastic action of some kind was called for. This came in the shape of knitted dungarees. Grannie was no knitter. Unless the pattern to be followed was all holes – so that she could drop as many stitches as she liked and no one would notice – Grannie left well alone.

This was different. Apart from it being a case of principle, it was also a matter of life and death. Grannie put her dislike for knitting to one side. She began the challenge of a lifetime – to knit a chicken a pair of trousers.

All in the cause of comfort, Grannie used the very best fluffy Angora wool. To be in the height of fashion, the colour she chose was brilliant fire-engine red! (As Grandad said, "that's so's the hens can see 'im a'comin' when 'ee gits better.")

The pattern was taken from the childrens' section of *Women's Own*. It was for a pair of dungarees for a two year old. It consisted of knitted trousers, with shoulder straps held in place with yellow buttons. Grandad looked at Grannie's efforts and winced.

"I 'opes the bleedin' neighbours 'ent goin' ter see 'im in that bloody lot," he said. "Like as not they'll think you've given birth ter a kid that looks like a bloody cockerel!"

Grannie ignored his rude remarks and battled on. She made constant alterations to the pattern as she went along. In the end, although a bit lop-sided, with one leg longer than it ought to have been, Grannie had evened things out by making the strap on the other side three inches longer.

Eventually the dungarees were finished. Grannie showed them to Grandad. He got his pained look and said, "apart from their cock-eyed look, 'ee won't cut much of a dash with them yeller buttons. I'm buggered if the whole bloody outfit 'ent enough ter put any self-respectin' hen orf 'er stroke."

Grannie glared at him, and hung her championship cockerel, who Grandad had now christened 'Trousers', back in the apple tree, resplendent in his new dungarees.

He certainly became the centre of attraction with the hens. It would seem that the combination of his hairy, fire-engine red dungarees, and the ghastly yellow buttons, could be said to have tickled their fancy. The hens turned on the charm – they were constantly standing in a circle, preening themselves and metaphorically 'fluttering their eyelashes'. 'Trousers' began to take an interest. This was encouraged by Grannie who placed his corn so that he had to make an effort to reach it.

Grannie's efforts were rewarded. It was noted that first thing in the mornings, 'Trousers' did not know whether to go after the corn or the hens. The first signs of life were returning. After a further consultation, Grannie and Grandad decided on a trial run. Grandad would take him up to the orchard first thing the next morning and watch points.

And so it was, that at seven o'clock on a fine September morning, Grandad took 'Trousers', in his new fluffy dungarees with yellow buttons, up to the top orchard and, after adjusting his shoulder straps, let him go.

Grandad appeared a while later with a twinkle in his eye.

An agitated Grannie, who was sitting on pins in the cottage, could not contain herself. "Wot 'appened, Will?" she said.

"Well," said Grandad, "I did as yer told me to, I gits 'is straps adjusted, pointed 'im at the hens, and let 'im go."

"Wot 'appened then?" said an expectant Grannie.

"Well, you know as 'ow yer is always sayin' as 'ow I'm allus makin' built-in design faults?" said Grandad.

"Yes!" said an irritated Grannie, "Git on with it!"

"Well," said Grandad, "If you was ter go up ter the top orchard this very minute, you'd see that bloody cockerel o' your'n, holdin' down that fattest Rhode Island hen, and a'kickin' up bloody hell's delight, 'cos you forgot ter put any flies in 'is bloody trousers!"

CHAPTER TWELVE

Home Affairs

Grannie's lot was not a happy one, particularly when it came to cooking. The sweet young things of today would not believe what was involved in the preparation of any food.

Grannie had four methods by which she could heat anything. The first was the top of an open fire. The second was the oven at the side of it. The third, an oil stove, which was situated in a pantry like the black hole of Calcutta. The fourth was an *Aladdin* heater that, together with the open fire, served to heat irons for pressing clothes, and for heating the overnight kettle.

The open fire was the only part of the kitchen range hot enough to boil saucepans on. This was a risky business. The open top had odd bits of metal on which to stand things; these were two bent pokers, a bit of old door hinge, and some wire mesh that Grandad had found in the shed. It was on this collection of scrap-iron – providing that the lot did not collapse (as if often did) when two saucepans and a kettle were placed on it – that Grannie performed wonders in the art of cooking.

The oven was another matter. The large hot-plate on the top was only ever warm enough to stand plates on. The temperature in the oven itself was dependant on the state of the fire. It was either so hot that it burned every-

97

thing to a crisp, or only tepid enough to cook pastry to pure-white concrete. The state of the fire was governed by what Grannie required of it. If it was a case of heating the irons on the front to press Grandad's shirts, then a fierce heat was called for. This burned everything in the oven to a frazzle. If a gentle simmer was required, perhaps for steaming a suet pudding, then nothing in the oven ever cooked.

It was all very difficult. It was then that emergency measures were called for. Grannie's second line of defence would be deployed. The oil stove in the pantry would be lit, and the suet pudding put where the heat could be regulated to a gentle simmer.

The use of the oil stove was fraught with problems. It was kept standing in a tin tray. Because Grannie could not see in the blackness of the pantry when she had overfilled the thing with paraffin, it was always one-inch deep and smelled awful.

The wicks were never trimmed (Grandad's job), with the result that they always 'burned-up' in the draught from the broken mica windows (which it was his job to repair but never did). The smoke burned the ceiling black and filled the room with minute flecks of floating soot which always seemed to contaminate the mashed potatoes.

Saucepans and kettles standing over open fires build up vast deposits of soot. It must be realised that it is not possible to immerse soot-laden saucepans in hot water. They had to be filled with hot,soapy water and only the inner surfaces washed. The soot-laden saucepans were stored in the pantry, and these, added to the abundance of soot from the oil stove. The buckets of coal that stood in the corner, added to the general feeling of depression when entering Grannie's pantry.

But there was worse to come. If Bryan said to me when we sat down to lunch, "Don't touch the Brussels sprouts, Derek, she's used the grey enamel saucepan to cook 'em in!" it signalled a fate worse than death. We both had to pretend that we had gone off Brussels sprouts. This would cause a court of enquiry by Grannie, who wanted to know what was wrong with her sprouts. The simple fact was, that she used the grey enamel saucepan to boil the snotty handkerchiefs in. There was no way that Bryan or I would eat anything that came out of *that* pot.

The 'Valor' stove that stood in the centre of the room served several purposes. It provided a form of central heating. It would be positioned in the middle of the living room, with a clothes-horse next to it, draped with wet clothes; these would steam gently, to be taken off and ironed with an iron that had been heating up on the top. An iron would only press one garment before it cooled off. Therefore Grannie had two irons, the second of which would be standing on the front of the fire. She would replace the first iron on the 'Valor' stove and change it for the other iron that was cherry-red on the front of the fire. Grannie would spit on the base of this to see how hot it was. The soot would have to be rubbed off on the coconut matting before any attempt was made to actually press clothes.

Before we all retired to bed, the 'Valor' stove would be taken upstairs and placed between the two bedrooms. Apart from the comforting glow from its tiny, red windows, the kettle would stand on it in winter, to provide hot water to thaw the outside tap for Grannie to make tea in the mornings; it would take all night to boil. Grannie's lot, indeed, was not a happy one.

Washing-up was also a nightmare. Grannie's life seemed to consist, in great part, of staggering in and out with great buckets of water and coal, or paraffin cans and bowls of washing-up; it was the latter that caused a particular problem.

Bert Parks was instrumental in the reason for the problem, it was Grannie who caused it. Bert Parks, when he was the landlord of the *Rock and Fountain*, had started the manufacture of radio sets in the back room of the pub. Grandad had never heard anything like it. He came home to Grannie in awe, "Christ!" he said, "'Ow 'ee gits them little buggers in there, I'll never know, but I'll tell yer wot, I'm a'goin' ter make one of them if its the last thing I do."

The bug really bit him. He bought every radio magazine in sight. The house was full of condensers and fuse wire; the place reeked with the odours of flux and solder. Grandad pored over electrical circuits and valves. In the end he proudly proclaimed that he thought that he had built a crystal set. It was basic in its construction; it seemed to consist of only five constituent parts. He and Alec, the eldest of the Stevens boys (three little brothers that he and Grannie had adopted), sat back and viewed their handiwork with pride. It became apparent that the crucial matter was to gently adjust a very fine, copper wire, known as a cat's whisker, so that it barely touched the surface of a crystal. This was a very acute and delicate operation.

Both Alec and Grandad were sharing a single pair of earphones, with an earphone held to their respective ears. Grandad fiddled with the cat's whisker. The air of concentration on their faces could only be described as tense; you could have heard a pin drop.

At one moment their faces lit up; Grandad shouted, "Got the bugger!" And promptly lost it again. After ten more minutes of fiddling, once again their expressions showed that something was coming through.

"Christ!" exclaimed Grandad in wonder "''ark at that lot!" Alec said that it sounded like the news; evidently an important announcement was about to be made concerning the King. They sat and waited for a news item that was going to be 'hot off the press' so that Grandad could tell the whole of the village before anyone else.

At the precise moment that the announcement was being made, Grannie, coming in with a bowl of washing-up, knocked the table, jogged the cat's whisker, and lost the signal.

Grandad exploded. "Christ, woman!" he said, bristling with fury, "wot the 'ell did yer bloody well do that fer? Now we'll never know wot's up with the bloody King!"

Grannie stood perplexed, mouth agape. "Wot yer on about?" she said.

"On about?" said Grandad, who always repeated the question in moments of stress. "I'll tell yer wot I'm bloody well on about, it took me best part of a bloody hour ter git the news on the BBC, and right at the vital part – when we woz a'goin' ter git the news on the King – you up and jogs the bloody table and we lost 'im. That's wot I'm on about!"

Grannie pouted. "Yer shouldn't be a muckin' about on the table when I've got work ter do," she snapped. "If yer wants ter play with them 'lectric toys, the shed's the place ter be!"

"'Lectric toys!" bellowed Grandad, hopping about like a cat on a hot tin roof, "that 'ent no bloody toy, that there's goin' ter cause a revolution!"

"Seems like it already has," said Grannie, looking decidedly narked. "Pity it can't give the mangle a revolution or two instead of clutterin' the damn table up; might 'elp fings along a bit fer me instead."

With that she staggered on her way to the pantry, leaving Grandad hopping mad that she should have stopped the development of the greatest innovation known to man.

Grannie constantly stopped this greatest innovation known to man. She was blamed whenever Grandad lost the station, for either slamming the pantry door or dropping the coal bucket with a bang. He even shouted at her for coughing at the wrong time, and for sneezing and making him jump just as he was making a critical adjustment. The radio was not good news as far as Grannie was concerned; it was the cause of constant friction between them.

In fact, it was a cause of constant friction between Grandad and the rest of the family. Everything had to stop for the six o'clock news. By now things had graduated to the earphones being placed in an enamel washing-up bowl. It seemed to amplify the sound "so that we could all hear," said Grandad. This was a total aberration on Grandad's part. The sound emitted from an earphone was at best, little more than the squeak made by a mouse. The result from both earphones in a tin bowl was equal to the noise made by two mice. It was completely unintelligible.

The fact that at tea time, all had to be conducted in church-like silence, whilst this faint squeaking came from a bowl placed in the middle of the table, caused Bryan and me to have hysterics. It was worse, when every two minutes Grandad would shout, "Wot's 'ee say?" When everyone tried to explain what it was that he had missed, it caused him to miss even more. It caused him great irritation.

It was bad enough getting a fit of the titters under normal circumstances; it was hell when Grandad had his thing about crystal sets.

Bryan had found something in a Christmas cracker. It was a joke that consisted of a small, flesh-coloured rubber plug, into which was inserted a dew-drop, four inches long, made of glass. It was designed to be inserted into the nose. It made it's owner look as if he had a really bad head cold. It was completely realistic. It was this, that Bryan, sitting with his back to Grandad, furtively slipped into his nose under the cover of his hand and said, "Look, Derek, I've forgotten my handkerchief!"

To say that I laughed would be incorrect. I exploded. Unfortunately I did this as Grandad was listening to a gardening programme on early potatoes. He hit the roof. The more irate he became, the worse it got. Bryan was beside himself with mirth with tears streaming down his face. I was rendered incapable of anything.

"Bloody well git outside and laugh it orf out there." said a testy Grandad. "Bloody kids don't know how ter behave these days!"

Bryan and I stood outside, holding our sides with laughter. We laughed until it was not possible to laugh any more.

When we had sobered up and regained our composure, we went back inside. We collapsed again when we saw Grandad crouched over the bowl, we were promptly sent back out again; somehow it did not seem so funny outside.

I got my own back on Bryan when we were having winkles for tea the following Sunday. Once again Grandad was crouched over the washing-up bowl, with this faint squeaking coming from its interior.

I took one of the black things from the end of a winkle, and stuck it on the end of my nose. I timed things to perfection. Bryan was drinking a cup of tea, when I quietly said, "Look, Bryan, I've forgotten my handkerchief!"

The result was catastrophic. He exploded. Two jets of hot tea shot from his nose – one from each nostril. They sprayed the whole of the table. Grannie's best tea-cakes, a plateful of brown bread and butter, and a bowl of trifle all caught it. So did I. Grandad shouted, Grannie shouted, both our mothers shouted. We were sent outside in hysterics, and in disgrace.

Luckily, another event took the heat out of the situation. Grannie, upset over Bryan spraying the cakes and trifle, started to clear the table. With a merry clatter, plates, cutlery, cups and saucers, all went in the bowl. It took but a second to pour a kettle of hot water over everything, and to liberally throw in a handful of soap flakes. Grandad appeared from looking for a new condenser in the bureau. "Where's me bloody earphones?" he said, looking at the washing-up bowl filled with hot water and soap flakes.

"Wot earphones?" asked Grannie.

"Them that was in the bloody bowl!" said Grandad.

"'Ent seem 'em!" said Grannie.

"You bloody well 'ave," said Grandad, "leastways yer would 'ave done, if you'd looked in the bloody bowl when you woz a fillin' of it!"

Grannie said, without much convition, "They weren't in the bowl when I puts the water in."

Grandad, looking snarled, said "I bloody well 'ope not!" Then added with incredulity, "Wot's them wires 'angin' over the side of the bowl?"

"Wot wires?" said Grannie.

"Christ, woman!" said Grandad. "Wot's wrong wiv yer

bloody eyes. You've gorn and drownded me bloody earphones, you 'ave!"

With that, he lifted the pair of earphones from Grannie's bowl of dirty washing-up water, and held them up as if they were a pair of dead kippers. With a sob in his voice he said "Now you've gorn an bloody well done it!"

Grannie, guilt in her every word said, "Never mind, duckie, it's only a bit of soapy water. 'Ang 'em up ter dry in front of the fire!"

Grandad said in high dudgeon, "I'd like ter bloody well 'ang *you* in front of the fire!"

A while later, when things had dried out a bit, Grandad and his brother, Ern, were sharing the earphones. They were listening to a string quartet.

"Sounds as if they is playin' under water!" said brother Ern.

"That's 'cos they're playin' bloody chamber music!" said an irate Grandad. At least it took the heat off Bryan and me.

Grandad decided to forget about cat's whiskers and make a real radio set.

Because of the continual Sunday tea-time hysterics when Grandad wanted to listen to the radio, Bryan's 'drip' joke was eventually thrown on the fire. I was banned from doing anything with winkles.

There were still times when things became uncontrollable. It was easy to achieve the same effect when Grannie served up rhubarb. Bryan would dangle a length from a rhubarb pie with a fork, and under the cover of his hand, hold it up to his nose and comment on his lack of a handkerchief. This would make me explode; once again we would have half-an-hour of choked laughter.

I suppose that all boys are awful, but what absolute horrors we must have been. Normal children simply blew up balloons to play with; we decided to do something different. What simpler than to hold the neck of a balloon over the outside tap, and to fill it with water.

The ructions that were caused when we pushed this wallowing object along the table towards Grannie, who could not work out what it was. She was putting knives and forks away at the other end of the table, as this strange purple thing, rolling from side to side, changing all the time from a sagging sphere to a pulsating dumbbell, relentlessly advanced on Grannie along the length of the table.

Grannie was a simple soul. Anything that she could not understand she viewed with fear. She was like this with visiting Indian traders, anyone cross-eyed, mice, balloons filled with water, and particularly anyone with a hump on their back. To her, a balloon should have been floating gently over the table, not rolling, like an alien visitation, all over the knives and forks in the drawer.

Peering intently through a cloud of cigarette smoke, Grannie tentatively prodded this strange thing with her finger. When it attempted to envelop her hand, she gave the most god-almighty scream, dropped a handful of knives and forks with a clatter, and gave it a colossal slam with a saucepan of custard that happened to be standing on the table at the time.

A domestic scene that had been one of calm and serenity, rapidly vanished as Grandad, who was sitting reading the *Picture Post*, leaped three feet in the air with the impact. Custard flew in all directions.

"Bloody top me!" he shouted, "Wot the 'ell's a'goin' on?" That was less than one tenth of a second before the balloon wallowed off the table and exploded on the floor.

Two pints of water does not normally seem very much. When it is less than a second behind a pint of Grannie's special lumpy custard, it seemed as if the whole world was covered with custard and water – which indeed it was. Grandad went mad.

Mind you, he had good cause. "Christ, woman!" he shouted, "look at all this bloody custard." He was sitting with it streaming down his spectacles. What was not covered in custard was drenched in water.

"It's only a little bit of water," said Grannie, still in shock from her confrontation with the balloon.

"No it bloody well 'ent!" roared Grandad, "It's bloody custard on me glasses, an' water everywhere else! Don't a'knows wot you're gittin' on about these days!"

"I only dropped the custard," said Grannie, realising that it was one of our pranks and covering up for us.

"If you only dropped the bloody custard, then how the 'ell is it that I'm covered from 'ead ter foot in water!" said an irate Grandad.

"Don't know where that come from," said Grannie. "I 'spects it come from me washing-up cloth."

"Christ!" said Grandad. "Now I'll catch me death, you see if I don't. Look at this bloody lot! I allus says that yer chucks too much bloody water about. Can't yer use a smaller cloth? Bloody fine state of affairs when a man can't sit by 'is own fireside without gittin' drowned."

Grannie stood with her foot on the remnant of the balloon until Grandad had stopped moaning and gone back to reading a dry copy of the *People*.

When he said "Hark at this, Ellie, it says 'ere *'They'll beat yer yet these Junkers, 'avin' beat 'arf the world by bloody murder, they'll beat the other 'arf, on their 'ands and knees beggin' fer mercy.'* I'm buggered if they 'ent right!" Grannie knew that the worst was past; she spirited the evidence away without Grandad knowing about it. Our little world reverted to its own ways, another episode passed into the oblivion of time.

Grannie had always aspired to great things when it came to anything to do with medication. She had cures that had to be experienced to be believed. The truth of the matter was, that because no one ever complained about an ailment after she had treated it, she assumed that her cure had worked; she did not realise, that in order to avoid her dreadful cures, one simply kept quiet, and hoped that things would sort themselves out.

Grandad, who was the main recipient of these treatments, seemed to thrive on them. He would encourage her by quoting articles from various farming magazines. The fact that these, more often than not, appertained to farm animals, was irrelevant. He and Grannie would enter into lengthy discussions on the attributes of the oil used for horse's hooves, and whether the same applications would be of any use for Grannie's corns.

CHAPTER THIRTEEN

Dr Bunwick's Patent Colon Irrigator

Grandad should have known better. He would, from time to time, appear with odd things that he had purchased from junk shops. On other occasions he would turn up with things which he had been persuaded to swop with the infamous Tommy Lee. One of these had been a rusty sewing machine that Grandad had swopped for a box of apples and renovated, with disastrous results, for Grannie. Another had been a pressure lamp that, apart from blinding us to varying degrees, had also caused partial deafness to all members of the family. He should have known better, therefore, when Tommy Lee took him one one side and, tapping the side of his nose with great confidentiality, said from behind his hand, "Knowin' as 'ow's Ellie's a one fer the medications, I've got summink 'ere that'll make 'er eyes sparkle!"

Grandad should not have been, but he was instantly interested. "Wot's that then, Tom?" he said.

"Tell yer wot," said Tommy Lee, "I'll take that pressure lamp and another box of apples, fer something that'll change yer life!"

Little did Grandad realise the truth of Tommy Lee's words.

Tommy Lee continued, "I 'ent a' goin' ter show it ter yer, 'cos it's brand new, an' still in the wrappin'. Ellie will knows 'ow ter use it, all she's got ter do is ter fill 'er up, an' give her a bloody good pump!"

Grandad wanted to get rid of the pressure lamp, which apart from causing great disruption in the family, was just plain dangerous. He did a deal with the lamp and another box of apples. Grannie was presented with an oval, brown-paper parcel that he assured her was going to be the the answer to all the family's medical problems. Grannie could not wait to examine the contents.

Removal of the brown-paper wrapping revealed what had once been a white oval box. This was similar in size to a small hat box. It had never been opened. Tommy Lee had bent the truth slightly. It had obviously been brand-new once upon a time, but that had probably been thirty years earlier. The once-white, glossy cardboard now had an unhealthy yellow pallor. The label on the lid announced it to be *Dr Bunwick's Patent Colon Irrigator*. The title of its contents stood out in grand Victorian script. It said simply, like the name of some Greek tragedy, *The Enema*.

There was a line illustration in the centre of the label which caused Grannie some problems. Not wishing to show her ignorance she pretended to know what it was. The truth of the matter was that *no one* knew what it was. Grannie studied the illustration which seemed to show a tube with a funnel at one end, a bulge in the centre, and a strange end-piece, rather like an old-fashioned clothes-peg but with several holes in it. Grannie looked knowledgeable but wary.

"'Ow does yer work it then, Ellie?" said Grandad expectantly.

Grannie said knowingly, "Best let's 'ave a look first, it's different ter the one I used afore."

Grannie opened the box and was confronted by a

three-foot length of half-perished rubber tube with a
bulge in the centre. There was a glass funnel, and a
strange orange section with holes in the sides. It looked
as if it was designed to be inserted in one end of the tube.

Grannie did not look too sure of herself. Grandad was
suffering a severe lack of confidence. After studying the
book of instruction, and with many references to
Grandad's dictionary, Grannie assembled the various
pieces.

"There!" she said, "that's about it. Now we're ready
fer action!"

"Wot sort of action?" said Grandad looking decidedly
apprehensive. "Wot the 'ell's it fer?"

Grannie was now in full command. "Ter put tea in!"
she proudly proclaimed.

"Bloody funny teapot,' said Grandad. "I'd a soon as
'ave mine in the ol' china one."

"Not the way this'un operates," said Grannie. "This
'ent fer taking tea like yer usually does. This is fer takin'
medicinal tea!"

Grandad looked even more worried. "Wot does I do
then?" said Grandad, "drinks it through the spout?"

Grannie now had a gleam in her eye. "No!" she said,
"There's more ways ter be takin' tea than thru' the
spout!"

"Don't a'knows if I'm any too keen on medicinal tea,
anyhow," said Grandad.

Grannie replied "You 'ent got no choice. When the
devil drives, needs must! If yer 'ent feelin' too good,
then you're a'goin' ter git the medicine!"

What convinced Grannie that the use of this instru-
ment was for the administration of tea, was indirectly
because of Grandad. Only a week before, he had read to
her an article from a farming magazine on the relative

attributes of caffeine. *Caffeine* it said, was an alkaloid. Not only was it noted for its stimulating properties, but also for its calming influence in bowel disorders. It was also said to have *great curative properties.* The magazine stated that *it had been noted to have an extraordi - nary effect* (it did not state what) *on horses.*"

In Grannie's medical book, the section on constipation was enlightening. It said that a common cause of constipation was dyspepsia. It also said that the treatment for this condition was the administration of an alkaline. Tea contained caffeine which was an alkaline. Grannie's diagnosis for the treatment of constipation was a nice cup of tea. How it was to be administered was another matter.

From that moment on, she watched Grandad like a hawk. At all times of the day she would enquire as to his welfare. She would constantly ask whether he had 'bin or not?'

"No, I bloody well 'ent!" he would reply testily. It was obviously a waiting game.

Grannie was wriggling with anticipation to try out her new acquisition. Grandad was not quite sure what her game was. He did not appear to be over keen to find out.

It was only a matter of time before Grandad, who was by nature a moaner, fell hook, line and sinker, for Grannie's carefully laid trap.

"You're lookin' a shade peekie, duckie," she said one Sunday afternoon. "Why don't you go upstairs an' 'ave a lay down on the bed. I'll bring yer a nice cup of tea up."

Grandad looked up in surprise and said, obviously with romantic thoughts in mind, "that's a nice thought, Ellie," and added as an afterthought, "yer can bring the *News of the World* up as well!"

As he went expectantly upstairs, little did he realise the pleasures that he had in store.

Grannie made a pot of tea, and placing the teapot and Enema on a tin-tray, disappeared up the staircase. We heard Grandad calling in a honeyed voice, "Hurry up, Ellie, I'm a'waitin'.'"

Because of the construction of the house, and the fact that Grannie was hard of hearing, it was quite possible to hear any conversation downstairs. As in the case of Grandad's brother, Ern, and the visit by the doctor, we sat with bated breath and listened intently. It was Grandad's first words that caused a few smiles. "Yer 'ent brought the milk and sugar up!" he said.

"That's 'cos I 'ent brought it up fer yer to drink," said Grannie mysteriously.

"Wot's that supposed ter mean?" asked Grandad, his voice troubled, adding "Wot's that bloody enema fer?"

"Ter take yer tea out of." said Grannie. "Yer is lookin' peekie an' complainin' of constipation, this is goin' ter be just the ticket!" There was a certain amount of scuffling with Grandad shouting "git that thing away from me! I 'ent bloody well 'avin' none of it."

This was followed by Grannie saying in a very determined way, "Oh yes you are! You're a damn pansy! You're the one as says it'll be the cure fer all things. Now turn over and git ready for action."

There was an ominous silence, broken only by Grannie stirring the teapot. That was, however, until Grandad shouted, "Christ! Go careful wiv that bloody thing, you'll scald me ter death!"

This outburst was caused by the fact that Grannie had assembled the contraption the wrong way round. It would appear that the bulge in the middle of the pipe was a pump with a one-way valve. With the clothes-peg end situated in an unmentionable part of Grandad's anatomy, and the funnel filled with hot tea from the teapot, the first time that Grannie, in Tommy Lee's words, 'gave it a bloody good pump' things went dreadfully wrong. The tea, instead of soothing Grandad's problems, seemed to make them drastically worse. Instead of gently inducing a calming influence of warm tea, it shot back up the funnel and all over Grandad!

There was a period of calm, whilst Grannie re-arranged things and started again. By this time we were in hysterics. Grandad was moaning all the time about Tommy Lee. "I'll shoot that bugger next time I see 'im," he said. "You see if I bloody well don't!" This was punctuated by a yelp, and Grandad shouting, "Bloody top me! This is worse that the Chinese water torture!"

A concerned Grannie said, "Wot's the matter, duckie, is it too 'ot fer yer?"

"Course it bloody well is," shouted Grandad. "I 'ent complainin' 'cos yer left the bloody sugar out!"

"I thinks I'll try a drop of milk ter cool it orf a bit," said Grannie.

"No yer bloody well won't!" exploded Grandad. "I've 'ad enough of this." With that we heard a thump or two, a clatter as the window at the top of the stairs was thrown open, and a crash, as Dr Bunwick's Patent Colon Irrigator landed in the middle of the lawn.

Grannie appeared in the living room and said that she had "given father a nice cup of tea." She asked if anyone else fancied a cup. There were no takers. She could not understand why we were helpless with laughter.

Grandad never complained again of flatulence or constipation. Grannie was happy, that without a shadow of a doubt, her treatment had worked like magic. In fact, it seemed that it had provided a life-time cure for Grandad.

There was, however, a strange conclusion to this affair. The next time that Tommy Lee came clattering by with his donkey and cart, he was met at the gate by a testy Grandad. He said that he wanted a word.

His word turned out to be several hundred. "If you fancy gettin' the arse shot out of yer trousers, try another caper like that!" he said. "If I ever meets Dr Bunwick in person, I'll personally give 'im a nice cup of tea, only this time he would give it the same way that Ellie had done, complete with the bloody teapot!"

Grannie heard him shouting from up the garden. She appeared with Dr Bunwick's enema. Grandad swopped it for some bicycle pedals and a shoe last. It was these items that were to cause Freddy Gregory some awful problems.

CHAPTER FOURTEEN

The High Life

It was a normal sequence of events, for the odd neighbour to pass the time of day in the shed with Grandad and to sample his latest batch of beer. This could be on a Saturday afternoon or any evening during the week.

On one occasion there happened to be two visitors sampling beer – Grandad's friend, Jimmy Trigwell, who was showing Grandad how to repair shoes on the last obtained from Tommy Lee, and Freddy Gregory, who was a cripple, and a lifelong friend of Grandad.

Grannie had mixed feelings about Freddy Gregory. Bearing in mind her attitude to anyone cross-eyed, or even worse, hump-backed, I suppose it was understandable that she should have had doubts about Freddy Gregory and the fact that he had one leg shorter than the other. She would nod and wish him well, but scuttle away as fast as her legs could carry her. She said that it made her feel sea-sick, to see him rocking along the lane to the bus stop.

It was therefore logical, that the combination of several pints of beer, Grandad's expertise in the manufacture of bicycles, Jimmy's craft in shoe repairing, and Freddy's crippled leg, that events should turn out the way that they did.

It was Grandad, in a rare state of alcohol induced

benevolence, that made the suggestion, that the bicycle pedals obtained from Tommy Lee, could well be the means of a drastic improvement in Freddy's life style. He said that with one leg shorter than the other, it was impossible for Freddy to ride a bicycle. He had been considering things he said, and felt that with his expertise, combined with the pedals supplied by Tommy Lee, he could make a machine that Freddy would be able to ride. The fact that Freddy was unable to ride a bicycle, and had no sense of balance whatever, was irrelevant. Grandad was going to design a machine that would enable him to achieve his wildest dreams. Sadly, what Grandad did not tell him, was that he was going to 'build-in' his customary design faults.

It was all to do with the fact that Tommy Lee's pedals must have come from an extraordinary high machine. The actual cranks of the pedals were six inches longer than normal. Grandad calculated that replacing the left side crank on a normal pair of pedals with one of Tommy Lee's long ones, would take up the slack needed for Freddy's short leg to push him along.

Jimmy Trigwell on the other hand, had other ideas. He reasoned – also through an alcohol induced haze, that he could make Freddy an invalid boot that would not only bring him up to the level of other people, but would also enable him to speed along on the bicycle that Grandad was going to make for him.

Whilst Grandad was looking for the appropriate parts to construct Freddy's bicycle, Jimmy was measuring him up for a new boot.

In the meantime, Freddy Gregory took lessons on how to ride a bicycle. These nearly always took place when the *Bo-Peep* closed at lunchtime on Saturday. It was Jimmy Trigwell who provided the bicycle that Freddy constantly crashed on. It became part of life at the *Bo-Peep*, to have a merry time at the pub, and to watch Freddy, nine sheets to the wind, being pushed on his way by a happy bunch of locals, firstly cheering him on, and then holding each other up, as Freddy wobbled through the nearest hedge.

Jimmy Trigwell, not pleased that his bicycle was being subjected to such treatment, worked at top speed to finish Freddy's special boot.

Jimmy – like Grandad – thought things through. He reasoned that Freddy's inability to balance, was probably brought about, because his left leg was shorter than his right. This fact alone, because he had more weight on one side than the other, made him unstable. He calculated that if he made Freddy's left boot considerably heavier than his right, it would cancel out the difference.

Anyone who knows the technology involved in the manufacture of surgical boots will tell you that the governing criteria is that of lightness. Most surgical boots have the core of the sole made from cork.

In the case of Freddy Gregory's boot, Jimmy Trigwell made the entire sole by nailing twenty sheets of leather together.

Apart from the fact that it shook the scales at over 10 lbs, he slightly overdid things. This made Freddy taller on the left side. He now limped the other way. Jimmy said it was a good thing. "Give it time, it'll wear down and things will even themselves out a bit!" he said.

Grandad, meanwhile, all in the cause of economy, used all the odd bits of bicycles that he had accumulated over the years. The frame came from a ladies bicycle that Grandad had built for Grannie. Grandad had spirited this away because (according to Grandad), she had got the speed bug and was the most dangerous thing on two wheels in Kent. Because it was a ladies bicycle there was no crossbar. It was thought that this would be better for Fred. Instead of trying to fling his overweight boot over a crossbar, he could get it through the hole in the middle instead.

The only handlebars that Grandad had, were the dropped ones that came from the wreck of Syd Forman's racing bicycle. The whole thing was made more incongruous by the fact that the saddle came from an old *Walls Ice-cream* tricycle. It was huge, and surmounted two massive coil springs which, combined with Freddy's uneven pedalling action, gave the whole thing the action of a comic cycle at the circus. Five pints of mild and bitter did not help very much either. Sergeant Carver turned a blind eye to the proceedings.

After several dreadful accidents, Freddy Gregory finally mastered the art of Grandad's bicycle. The time had come for Grandad to fit his masterpiece of ingenuity. He bolted on the long crank to Freddy's left-hand pedal. All was ready for action. To celebrate the launch, a drink was called for at the *Bo-Peep*.

Five pints later, with an air of great confidence and his hat on sideways, Freddy Gregory was lifted onto his steed and his feet placed on the pedals. With a cheer he was pushed on his way by the locals.

It was at this point that one of Grandad's notorious design faults became apparent. Whilst Freddy's foot was perfectly positioned on the pedal when it was at its highest point, there was nothing but six inches of air between his boot and the pedal when it reached its lowest. Freddy got into a speed wobble, and fell off!

Grandad became extremely agitated with some of the locals when he caught them laughing because his design had gone wrong. He said that Freddy was "just plain bloody awkward!" The fact that poor Fred was laying propped up against the pub wall with whisky being administered was neither here nor there.

It was now that Jimmy Trigwell, with a bit of a wobble on, and like the United States cavalry, came to the rescue. "Stand back!" he said with authority. "I've got summink 'ere that'll show yer wot it's all about."

Grandad, smarting from his failure said, "And wot the 'ell do you know about pedals!"

"I don't know anything about pedals, but I bloody well know more than you do about feet!" said Jimmy Trigwell smugly.

With that he produced a brown paper parcel and commenced to unwrap it. Everyone stood with bated breath, waiting for Jimmy's answer to what seemed an insurmountable problem. With a flourish Jimmy unveiled his masterpiece, all 10 lbs of it.

"Christ!" said Freddy Gregory, "It's a bit big innit?"

"Made ter measure!" said Jimmy

With a struggle they managed to get Freddy's left boot off. With an even greater struggle they managed to get the oversize one on.

Several willing helpers lifted him up as others straightened his bent front forks. It was when they tried to walk him to his machine that it became apparent that Grandad was not the only one capable of design faults. Such was the weight of Freddy's new boot that he seemed unable to walk. He seemed fixed to the ground.

Jimmy Trigwell, undaunted, lifted the overweight boot, complete with Freddy's foot, and said, "You'll go like greased lightnin' when yer leg muscles build up!"

It was a combined effort. Grandad, Jimmy, and five others managed to get a battered Freddy into the saddle.

With a rousing cheer from all the customers at the *Bo-Peep*, he was given a high-speed send off down the lane.

It was Freddy's first attempt to pedal that caused the accident. He pushed off with his right foot. As his left foot, the one that was now six inches higher thanks to the longer crank and oversized boot, came up, it jammed poor Freddy's knee with great force against the underside of the racing handlebars. The knee was ripped from Freddy Gregory's trousers as he went over the top.

He actually hit the bank on the corner of Hollybush Lane. After smashing what was left of the sign that Grandad had erected when we did Sunday afternoon teas, he landed in the potato patch near to the top orchard.

Freddy was carried home suffering from abrasions and concussion. According to Grandad, after five pints of mild and bitter and several whiskys, this was highly debatable.

Dr Grant was summoned from Orpington. He confirmed the diagnosis, but was puzzled at what seemed to be a partial paralysis in Freddy's left leg. It had never been particularly strong, but Dr Grant could find no reason for its apparent weakness. He said that physiotherapy, in the form of weight lifting with that particular leg would probably be of some help. Freddy kept very quiet. He knew that he could cure the problem in ten seconds flat. He did this by throwing Jimmy Trigwell's surgical boot violently in the dustbin!

There was, however, a strange sequel to this event. Grandad would never give up on a problem. He smarted at being laughed at in the *Bo-Peep*. He gave Freddy's crippled leg deep thought. Once more banging came from the shed. Grandad came up with the answer. Freddy Gregory was not a proud man – which was just as well.

Although Grandad's contraption could only be used locally, nevertheless it solved the problem. Freddy Gregory went back to his original boot. For the next few years he could be seen in the lanes around Maypole, flying along at high speed, propelled by his good leg on the ground, and his short leg on a wooden scooter, made by Grandad particularly for that purpose.

It was a very practical solution that restored Grandad's reputation.

CHAPTER FIFTEEN

Well Hill Church

When it came to religious instruction, Bryan and I were left very much to our own devices. The important thing seemed to be, that we got out from under Grandad and Grannie's feet on a Sunday afternoon. The truth of the matter was, that they both wanted an undisturbed snore-up for two hours, and either church or Sunday School was an excuse to get us out of the way.

This being the case, we naturally chose the establishment that best suited our intentions at the time. If it was a Sunday afternoon in the winter, and the lanes were deep with snow, then sledges would be the order of the day. It would be Well Hill Church that would be attended, not because of any great religious fervour, but because sliding was more important. Well Hill Church happened to be at the top of the hill.

Another factor that made the little church desirable, was the reputation of its respective football and cricket teams. When either of these were doing well, it was a fight to get in the church. Again, this had nothing to do with religious fervour, simply a means to get in a good local team.

Another reason for our interest in Well Hill Church was the fact that Mr Moorbey, the kindly old Lay Reader who ran things, organised his own version of the Boys

Brigade. They wore black and white pill-box hats with a badge on the front and black leather belts with leather pouches on the side. These were at a premium, we would have killed for them.

The little church was a white, wooden-boarded building in the colonial style. It had a green, corrugated-iron roof. This had an overhang at the font with housed the most depressing bell ever heard. It rang with a deathly clunk, more to warn people away than to invite them to holy worship. A porch over a side door completed a picture of the prettiest of places on a spring morning, but did nothing to keep out the howling wind on the most exposed place in Kent. It was quite possible to stand in Well Hill Church on a winter's afternoon and freeze to death.

Mr Moorbey was a mild-mannered man who meant well. Sadly, he was *too* nice. He was bossed about by an elderly spinster known as Kate Forman, who, like her counterpart at the chapel in Chelsfield, was *really* the one in charge. She occupied a seat next to the bell rope. She would sit, unsmiling, severe, with no sense of humour, and toll the bell with monotonous regularity. Kate Forman was probably the originator of the curfew that tolled the knell of passing day. According to Grandad "she would also 'ave a bloody good row wiv anyone who pinched her chair!"

Mr Moorbey was also bullied to an enormous extent by Mr Jefferys, the mainstay of the congregation.

Mr Jefferys stood at the back, and gave his rendering of any hymns being sung. A definition in the *Oxford Eng - lish Dictionary* quotes the word 'render' as 'to tear asunder'. That is precisely what Mr Jeffreys did. He ripped asunder any hymn. He bellowed rather than sang; he accompanied himself with his own metronome – he kept time by smashing the wooden floor of the church with a massive walking stick. He inflicted concussion on the congregation.

Mr Jeffreys would also constantly interrupt the service by bellowing at poor Mr Moorbey to "Speak up, man! We can't hear you at the back!" He made more noise than the rest of the congregation put together.

The organ was played by Mrs Jeffreys. She was all that her husband was not. Mrs Jeffreys was tall, elegant, and refined. She wore the most delicate of black lace dresses, her hair was short, white, and well coiffeured, she smelled vaguely of lavender. She was like a calm summers evening.

The tiny organ was Mrs Jeffreys domain. All was tranquillity and peace at her end of the church. It was hell at her husband's end.

There were times when the old man, with the most awful discord, hit a wrong note or two. These must have stretched her saintliness to the limit, but she looked serene and ploughed on, albeit with a wince or two, but smiling saintly nevertheless.

As far as we were concerned, the most important part of the church was the hut at the back. This, like the church, was a white, wooden building.

It was the place where all the decisions were made concerning team selections for the football and cricket clubs.

It was here that Mr Moorbey gathered his flock. It was also, sadly, the place where awful plans were made in connection with the Boys Brigade.

Mr Moorbey, all in the cause of the healthy upbringing and the religious instruction of his flock, decided that a spot of life in the open air was called for. A camping exercise was decided upon. He should have known better. The site chosen was a meadow along Well Hill Lane situated opposite to the small, wooden bungalow that was his residence. The idea was that we would sleep under canvas for the night and, under Mr Moorbey's direction, sing hymns around a camp fire. These were his intentions, not ours! To start with, everything went according to plan. The tent was duly erected, camp beds positioned. Mr Moorbey arrived and duly struck up with *Onward Christian Soldiers*. We wailed along behind him. This was followed by *The Old Rugged Cross* which seemed to go on forever. Our voices began to die at verse ninety-eight. Enthusiasm was beginning to wane. Our prayers were finally answered when our kindly host departed to his bed at nine o'clock.

It was then that things began to happen. Bob Hogben, Eric Sampson, and Bryan Yates disappeared into the night. They reappeared half an hour later, laden down with eggs. Mr Moorbey did not know it, but he had lent us a primus stove and saucepan. He also lent us eight eggs that he would have collected for breakfast from his hen coop. Before long they were bubbling away merrily on the stove.

Odd bars of chocolate were produced, together with a bottle or two of cider. We sat back ready to have a stolen feast when the eggs were done.

But the Lord moves in mysterious ways. The primus stove became blocked up. It was then that things began to go horribly wrong. Bob flicked the perforated dome from the top of the stove to try and sort out the blockage. It certainly did that. It set the tent on fire!

A jet of flaming paraffin, reminiscent of a flame thrower, hit the top of the tent. Fortunately, it was a bell tent and the flames were confined to the top. Panic ensued; we had time to get our things out, and rapidly

*Plate 14: Unclamping fodder-beet for Henry May at Hewitts Farm.
Albert Wadey, Dave Costin, 'Stodger' Wadey*

Plate 15: Threshing, a time of celebration. A 'Maypole' meadow scene

Plate 16: Some of the 'Maypole' boys. Playing in the meadow opposite to
Yewtree House

Plate 17: Mr Fox, the tomato expert, who gave organ instruction in the chapel

Plate 18: The Fire Station. Where Mr Hogben kept his equipment, and behind which the Five Bells *darts team held clandestine meetings*

Plate 19: Joey Turner, general dealer, owner of the fastest horse and cart in the village

Plate 20: The White House *also known as the* Chestnuts *or the* Pepper Pot. *Situated on the top of Well Hill with the best view in Kent. Two Poplar trees stood alongside known as 'Adam' and 'Eve'*

Plate 21: Arthur Checksfield, dealer in green grocery and hair-curlers? In the lane outside Yewtree House, *with donkey and cart sold to him by Tommy Lee*

Plate 22: Pen drawing of part of the living room in Yewtree House

Plate 23: The family on the lawn with gramophone in 1927.
Front: *the Stevens boys (Albert, Alec, and Syd).* Centre: *Dorrie and Alf Yates, Grannie and Grandad, Wilfred.* Rear: *Jim's sister Louise and Little Nell*

Plate 24: Imperial Airways airliner after forced landing in fields between Goddington and Chelsfield Church. (Note missing lower-half of port wing)

released the guy lines. The fire was put out by all of us, rather like red indians doing a fire-dance, on what was left of the top of the tent. The top three feet was burned completely out.

A glum discussion then took place as to what we were going to do. Reg Mitchell happily informed us that the tent belonged to Mr Jeffreys who had lent it to Mr Moorbey for the occasion. We were in the mire in a big way. The night air began to cool rapidly. We were sitting huddled in our blankets, it looked like being a long night. The thought of warm beds at home did the trick – we packed up. A smuggling session then took place as the primus stove and saucepan were replaced in Mr Moorbey's shed. Several hens objected strongly, as hard-boiled eggs were slipped back under them in their nesting boxes. Finally the tent was artfully folded so that the burned bit could not be seen, and packed away in its canvas bag. This was laid on Mr Moorbey's doorstep. We crept home to our respective parents, making the excuse that it was too cold to sleep the night in a tent.

When Mr Moorbey came visiting our homes the following day to find out what had happened to his flock, it was explained that the cold had caused us to abandon the exercise. We said that as it was late, we did not want to disturb him. He remarked at the size of the burned patch where the fire had been. He said that it should have kept us warm all night.

There were several sequels to this incident. Mr Moorbey was heard to make the observation in the grocers shop on Well Hill, that something was amiss with his hens. It would seem that they had taken to laying their eggs hard-boiled. Mr Moorbey said, that whilst this doubtless saved him from cooking them, it caused him problems when making cakes – the recipes that his mother had left him, did not cater for cake-making using hard-boiled eggs.

Strangely, the damaged tent did not come to light until the following summer. Mr Jeffreys did an impersonation of a roaring bull when he found it. He accused his wife (who was the gardener in the family) of leaving it too near to the bonfire. He ranted and raved, but she was used to this, she smiled serenely and told him to think of his blood pressure.

Mrs Jeffreys, however, knew that the tent had been nowhere near to the bonfire. From that moment on, she suspected Mr Moorbey of being underhand and not to be trusted.

It was an embarrassment when Mr Moorbey read the lesson on a Sunday. Any reference that he made to the 'Fires of Hell' or 'Fire and Brimstone', would cause Mrs Jeffreys to glare at him, and pointedly nod in an accusing manner. Mr Moorbey would blush furiously. This, in her eyes. made him look guilty. She was determined to get to the bottom of things.

It was this search for the truth, that caused my mother and me to have the most uncomfortable half-an-hour of our lives.

Once upon a time, many years before, my mother had been courted by Toby Jeffreys. Toby was the son of Mr and Mrs Jeffreys who lived in the first house at the top of the hill, in Well Hill Lane. Mr Jeffreys had been responsible for his son marrying someone else. This had been a business arrangement between him and his partner in a tea importers in the city – it kept things in the company. Toby had been the first love of my mother's life, he continued to meet her in secret until the eve of his wedding. Despite all this, Mrs Jeffreys had a great affection for my mother. I suspect that she did not really agree to this arranged liaison. They continued their friendship for many years.

Mrs Jeffreys invited my mother and me to her house for tea on a Saturday afternoon. Although it was a pleasant occasion, it soon became obvious that I was going to be questioned about the tent with a hole in the roof. Mrs Jeffreys had told my mother that she would like to take the opportunity to introduce us to the latest addition to the family, someone called Vincent, who was in the navy.

It was a beautiful day as we walked up their garden path. The view over Chelsfield village was impressive. It was possible to see Saint Paul's Cathedral in the city of London many miles away, the fields of the Garden of England were very soft and green.

After exchanging pleasantries, Mrs Jeffreys served brown-bread cucumber sandwiches. We had tea from a delicate, bone-china tea service. Life could not have been more pleasant or refined.

Eventually, Mrs Jeffreys broached the question of the condition of her husband's tent. The indications were that she was going to pointedly ask whether we had returned it to Mr Moorbey in good condition. This was going to put me on the spot. I could not let the old Lay preacher take the blame for the rest of his life, and we could not afford to replace the tent. It seemed a question to which I had no answer.

Mrs Jeffreys had reached the point of no return. I was sweating at the thought of being put on the spot for letting poor old Moorbey take the blame. Mrs Jeffreys had got the bit between her teeth; "I now have the embarrassing task of having to ask you a question concerning my husband's tent." I felt as if I was falling down a lift shaft with nothing to catch me at the bottom. I shut my eyes and waited for the *coup de grace*.

It never came. Mr Jeffreys, like a knight on a white charger, came to my rescue. He came into the room and shouted (Mr Jeffreys never spoke in a normal tone) "Haven't you introduced our guests to Vincent, my dear," adding, "He's in the navy, you know." I breathed a sigh of relief at his opportune intervention. Mrs Jeffreys, not particularly wishing her husband to know of her investigation, said, "No, dear, I thought he was in the garden with your."

For a moment the heat was off. I breathed a sigh of relief. I did not realise that I was about to be placed in a far worse situation.

Mr Jeffreys, with a voice like a fog-horn, bellowed at the top of his voice, "VINCENT! COME HERE!"

I can remember thinking it was hardly the tone or manner in which to address a member of the senior service.

It was at that point that Vincent appeared. At least a Pekinese dog dressed in a sailor suit did.

What was even more of a shock, was that it was even wearing a sailor's hat with the words HMS Victory emblazoned on it. I looked at my mother. She was purple with suppressed laughter.

"Come along, Vincent," shouted Mr Jeffreys, "show us your party trick.' Vincent promptly obliged. He balanced on his back legs and hopped all over the lounge.

By this time I had my handkerchief out and holding it to my nose, blew vigorously in an attempt to hide the peals of laughter that were building up within me. I noticed my mother doing the same.

Vincent then commenced to do all manner of things. At the behest of Mr Jeffreys he balanced on his front legs; this was spoiled somewhat by his hat continually falling over his eyes. He did somersaults and pretended to lie dead on the floor. At this point I rather hoped that he would. Regretfully the worst was yet to come.

Although this is a distasteful subject, it must be mentioned, in order to explain the reason for the next turn of events. It is obvious, due to our anatomy, that there are parts of our bodies that are difficult to reach – between the shoulder blades for example.

Usually, if a good scratch is required, we can either get someone else to do it for us, or employ the services of a back-scratcher. The situation is the same with other members of the animal kingdom, particularly dogs. The area particularly difficult to get at for a dog, is that unmentionable place at the back beneath the tail. When irritation occurs at that point, the only option open to a dog, is to sit on it, and punt itself along with its front legs, preferably on coconut matting. If the irritation is particularly intense, then this act is performed on whatever comes to hand. This was the case with Vincent.

Imagine the situation, therefore, when you are at exploding point over the antics of a Pekingese called Vincent, doing acrobatics in a sailor suit with *HMS Victory* on the hat, to find that he is performing a new trick quite unexpected by his owners.

Vincent leaped up on the arm of the settee (on which my mother and I were sitting at either end), and with his tongue hanging out and a look of pure delight on his face, proceeded to punt himself along at high speed. He did not stop there; he punted himself along the back and down the arm on my side as well.

I dared not look at my mother, she was making the most awful choking noises into her handkerchief.

"What the hell's that damned dog up to?" boomed Mr Jeffreys.

"Having a slide by the looks of things," said Mrs Jeffreys.

"Where did he learn that from, then?" said Mr Jeffreys, amazed at this new trick. "He didn't learn it from me!"

For a fleeting moment I had a vision of Mr Jeffreys in a sailor's hat, sliding along on top of the settee.

"No, my dear," said Mrs Jeffreys., "I would hardly think that he did!" The rest of the visit was spent with both my mother and me, purple in the face with suppressed laughter, trying to hold polite conversation, with this awful dog skating about all over the carpet.

I felt quite ill, I felt sure that I had done myself some internal injury. The worst part was trying to hold a conversation, and laughing in all the wrong places. When finally the afternoon pleasantries were over, and thankfully the mystery of Mr Jeffrey's tent forgotten about, we were seen off the premises by the old couple.

As we turned to wave farewell at the gate at the bottom of their garden, Vincent was skating at high speed, in ever decreasing circles, in the middle of their back lawn.

As we passed from view, Mr Jeffreys did not appear to be very pleased. He blustered in his customary loud voice, "Don't know where he gets all these bloody tricks from. He was over at old Moorbeys for the last few days, he must have learned it over there."

"Yes, my dear," said Mrs Jeffreys.

"'Spects he was the one who had the top out of my bloody tent, too!" said Mr Jeffreys.

Mrs Jeffreys smiled to herself, and said nothing.

CHAPTER SIXTEEN

Chelsfield Chapel

Apart from the little church on Well Hill, the other places of worship were the chapel, and Saint Martin of Tours, the main church in the area. While the attractions for the young bloods at the time at Well Hill Church were its football and cricket teams; with Mr Moorbey's Boys Brigade a close second, with the chapel in Chelsfield village it was quite simply a case of girls.

I suppose, that at the time that Chelsfield chapel was in its heyday, we were beginning to realise that there were other things in life besides football and cricket. Apart from the fact that our particular Sunday School teacher at the chapel was extremely attractive, all the village girls seemed to be there on a Sunday afternoon. Winter time seemed to have a special appeal of its own. The room that we used, was warm and smelled of stale furniture polish and musty hymn books. Initially, of prime importance was to get more gold stairs stuck on your attendance card than anyone else. If you did, you became the proud possessor of a coloured religious postage-type stamp, which pictured Jesus hanging on the cross. For some obscure reason this made you holier than anyone else. It consequently enabled you to lord it over your contemporaries. Apart from making you a pet of the good-looking Sunday School teacher, it also made you welcome by the god-fearing parents of attractive daughters. These would not normally have allowed you within a mile of their little angels. This simple religious stamp seemed to open all doors. I suppose that was the first real lesson that we learned from the chapel. There were real advantages to be had from the possession of religious stamps.

Whilst the actual chapel attendance was something to do on a Sunday afternoon – the really interesting part was what happened before and after.

Donald Widger had nothing. He was tiny of stature, regularly whacked by everyone in sight, and lived in the council houses. He ran everywhere at high speed. His presence was only ever required if we were short in the cricket or football team.

He was, however, causing us problems. We sensed that something was up by his manner. Not only was he walking about with a swagger, but he was being patted on the head by the teacher. He was also being invited by the parents of the best looking girls in the chapel into their homes. We smelled a rat.

Because he attended Sunday School with monotonous regularity, he accumulated almost a full attendance card of stars. We knew the place where the attendance cards were kept. As surreptitious check revealed that he had one more star on his card than we did.

It was a serious situation. Donald Widger had to be stopped at all costs. We could hardly prevent him from attending Sunday School – or could we?

Bryan and I had a discussion on the way to Sunday School. "We've got to stop the little bugger somehow!" said Bryan.

I agreed. The question was how? We devised a plan that necessitated a trip to Neal's Stores.

The following Sunday dawned bright and clear. After lunch we were spruced-up by our mothers, but waited for a saintly Donald Widger to pass by on his way to the chapel. We contrived to meet him at Maypole corner.

Donald happened to be very good at climbing trees. Bryan and I had arranged an argument about whether anyone could climb the tall elm trees that stood by the pond. Donald said that he could. We bet him that he could not.

"Wod'ger bet, then?" said Donald.

"I dunno," said Bryan.

"Wot about that chocolate yer mum giv' yer!" I said.

"That's special!" said Bryan "I ain't givin' that!"

"Go on!" I said. "She's got more where that come from."

Bryan agreed. Donald accepted. The trap was set.

Donald shinned up the tree like a squirrel, as we knew he would. He won his bar of chocolate and went merrily on his way across the fields eating it with great gusto.

We dawdled along behind looking pleased with ourselves. Bob and Reg (two of our contemporaries) met us outside the chapel. They were not looking happy.

"Wot's up wiv you two, then?" we asked.

"Widger's goin' ter git 'is last star terday!" said Bob.

"'Ee ain't got it yet!" said Bryan.

"There ain't no stoppin' 'im now," said Reg.

"Let's wait an' see." I said.

We sat and waited. Our attractive teacher read a lesson on cleanliness being next to godliness. Donald sat and wriggled. He kept putting his hand up to attract her attention. She was carried away with fervour and ignored him. Donald became flushed. In the middle of the Lords' prayer it happened. The teacher had just quoted the line "thy will be done on Earth as it is in

Heaven." Donald suddenly sprung to his feet and yelped "Christ!"

The teacher, thinking that her preaching had suddenly awakened an attack of religious fervour said, serenely, "Calm down, Donald," adding, "The Lord's will, be done on Earth!"

"If I don't git a move on," said Donald, "It'll be dun in me bloody trousers!"

A shocked congregation stood open-mouthed at such blasphemy.

Donald flew out of Sunday school as fast as his legs could carry him. He was holding his attendance card with one hand, and the seat of his trousers with the other.

He was heading for the sanctuary of the undergrowth in Skibbs Lane. Sadly he did not make it.

Donald came back for his star but was not allowed in. It was awarded at the end of every meeting. The teacher – holding her nose – told him that stars were awarded for attendance. As he had not been there, he was not entitled to it. He was not in any fit state to collect it anyway.

On the way home afterwards, a little group gathered at Jubilee corner.

"How did you manage ter do that, then?" asked Bob and Reg.

"There ain't much that a bar of chocolate won't do." said Bryan.

"Particularly when it's 'Ex-Lax!" I said.

We fell about with helpless laughter for the rest of the way home;

In the pecking order of things, Well Hill Church was a distinctly clap-boarded affair. It was not very far up the social scale. Chelsfield village was too far away for the people that lived on the Hill, they naturally gravitated to their own church.

The chapel, on the other hand, was the place used by most of the people in the village for holy worship. We were to discover that it was used for other purposes too. . . .

In order of religious status, Chelsfield Church, Saint Martin of Tours, was the top of the range. Only the upper echelons of village society worshiped there. For the commoner, it was the place to go to be christened, married, and buried. Otherwise, no one ventured over the other side of the main road. This seemed to be the boundary as far as we were concerned. You touched your forelock and kept your place. Your place was *not* Chelsfield Church.

The chapel was fully subscribed on a Sunday. The whole village would turn out in their best clothes. The men would be like trussed turkeys, with clip-on ties and shirts too small for them. They had tight suits with heavy turn-ups and brown boots. The women wore straw hats like baskets of fruit, black, tightly-laced shoes with lisle stockings, and drab dresses. They had sour looks with supercilious expressions. They sized up the clothes that the other women were wearing.

The sound of holy worship was not too good on the ear. It seemed that the organ in the main chapel, pumped by either Reggie Mitchell or 'Moggie' Tester, was in constant competition with the organ, furiously pumped as well as played, by Miss Bunn in the Sunday School at the room at the back. When both of these were going full blast on different hymns the cacophony would be indescribable.

Amongst the worshippers on a Sunday, one stood out as being the most god-fearing of all. His name was Mr

Fox. Mr Fox lived in a splendid house named *Hollycroft* situated in Hollybush Lane. This was a bridle path that ran along the top of our garden. Although being almost our nearest neighbours, Mr and Mrs Fox had a gardener and a maid. They were socially in a very different class to us.

To appreciate Mr Fox it is necessary to describe him in detail. He was of average height and walked with exceedingly short steps. He sported a white, neatly-trimmed, full beard in the style of King George V. He wore *pince-nez* spectacles and over his highly-polished, side-button boots he wore spats. His attire could only be described as immaculate. A half-length grey overcoat with a matching velvet collar would cover a delicately patterned waistcoat in the same shade of grey. His shirt had pearl buttons and a stiff collar with tips turned back. He wore a matching taffeta bow tie. He would carry a silver-topped walking cane.

On occasions, he and Mrs Fox would pass our cottage in a pony and trap. This would be either when he was attending the village school in his capacity as a visiting governor, or when he was on his way to services at 'The Temple' at St Mary Cray. He was well known there, and a staunch supporter of the high church practised at that establishment.

For other reasons, Grandad did not hold Mr Fox in very high esteem. The course of events proved Grandad right.

Miss Tester was a teacher at the village school. She was in complete contrast to Mr Fox, whom she barely tolerated. 'Moggie', as she was known by all the children, was without doubt, sinister. She had a foreboding look and was never known to smile. In stature she was all of six feet tall. She took size ten in shoes. Her dress sense could be said to be drab. With deep set eyes in a sallow complexion, topped by a bobbed hair style that went out of fashion years before, there was no way that she could be described as attractive.

It was obvious that 'Moggie' detested Mr Fox. She resented his interference in school matters, which she considered her prerogative

She would sniff with disdain when he visited the classroom and make it quite obvious that his presence was not required. It was all very embarrassing.

All in the cause of fun and games with the girls, we would hang about when Sunday School was over, and when the teacher had gone, have a merry old time before we went to our respective homes for tea.

This was soon noticed, however, and we were cleared away before any mischief could develop. We devised a plan to get over this problem.

At the back of the Sunday-School classroom stood a pile of pews. These were to replace older ones in the main chapel. They had been there for two or three years. They were waiting for Mr Smith, the builder, to install them when he had the time. There were also several packs of new hymn books and bibles.

The following Sunday we arrived at the chapel early. It took no time at all to re-arrange the pews so that they formed a perfect hiding place for several boys. The hymn books and bibles were used to plug the open spaces between the pews, to make a small room four feet square, in which we could hide.

At the end of the afternoon, when our teacher had gone to collect her coat from the cloakroom, we quickly nipped into our hiding place and waited. Before too long our teacher returned from the cloakroom and departed on the bus to Orpington. It was simplicity itself to undo the yale lock from the inside, slam the door as we left, and have a merry time with the girls in the village street, before they went home. We laughed at the ease of the operation and of merry times to come. The following Sunday we sat like angels. We waited for our teacher to collect her coat.

At the appointed hour, she duly disappeared to the ladies cloakroom to collect her coat. Slamming the door behind her, she once again departed to catch the bus to Orpington.

We were about to come scrambling out of our hidey-hole behind the pews, when we heard a door opening and closing, and the sound of footsteps. Someone had entered the classroom from the main chapel. We sat and waited with baited breath for them to go away.

After a while we were amazed to hear someone practicing on the organ. We came to the conclusion that whoever it was, they had no idea of how to play. They were striking several keys at the same time with no recognisable hymn being played. It seemed to go on and on.

It was Eric Sampson who had the brilliant idea of slipping out one of the new hymn books from between the pews, so that he could see what was going on. When he did, he sat with his mouth open.

"Wot's goin' on?" we whispered.

"I'm buggered if I know!" he said.

"Wot's all the music, then?" we hissed.

" 'Moggie' Testers on the organ," he said.

"Wot, playin' it?" we said.

"Nah!" said Eric, "Sittin' on it."

"Yer can't play an organ sittin' on it." we said.

"No," said Eric. "Leastways, not wen ol'-man Fox is a 'sittin' on yer!"

Bob pushed him out of the way, "Let me 'ave a look," he said. In turn *his* mouth fell open. "Christ!" he said, "Wot's he up to then?"

Bryan had a look. "Doin' a bit of organ pumpin' I 'spects," he said.

Stan Wickenden peered through the gap. "He's still got his trilby hat on," he said. "She ain't never goin' ter learn facin' that way!"

"Whatever she's doin'," said Bob, "She's 'appy about it! I've never seen 'er smile so much in all me life."

Eventually the music stopped. The organ ran down with a groan. We sat in our hiding place stunned. We had never seen anything like it.

Mr Fox disappeared down the village street with a sprightly step, and 'Moggie' Tester went back to the main chapel, looking radiant.

Whatever they had been doing, it seemed to have agreed with them. We talked about it all the way home.

It was over tea that we broached the subject with Grannie and Grandad.

"Can yer learn the organ, sittin' on it an' facin' the wrong way?" Bryan asked Grandad.

"Not unless you're a bloody acrobat," he replied.

"Wot about if someone woz a'sittin' on yer lap?" we asked.

"I couldn't play it sittin' the right way round," said Grannie, "leastways not with Father on me lap. Why does yer ask, duckie?"

" 'Cos 'Moggie' Tester woz learnin' that way in the chapel, wiv Mr Fox sittin' on 'er lap!" we exclaimed.

"Christ!" said Grandad, losing himself behind his newspaper. "I knowed 'ee woz smart, but that's a bloody trick that I'd never a'thought of!"

Grannie had shot into the pantry and broke a plate. She

re-appeared as white as a sheet. "P'raps 'ee was doin' the pumpin'," she said, in an unfortunate choice of words.

"I'll say 'ee bloody well woz!" chortled Grandad, "damned ol' hypercrit, bet ol' Mrs Fox don't know 'ee's in the music business!"

"You 'ent got nuffink ter sing about," snapped Grannie. "It weren't too long ago you woz a'tryin' ter git a merry tune out of an ol' fiddle, and an ugly one at that!" (This was a reference to an incident at the *Bo-Peep*, when Grandad had been caught-out trying to be over-friendly with the landlords cross-eyed sister.)

Grandad kept as quiet as a mouse. Grannie had set about him with a walking stick on that occasion. It was an incident that he wanted to forget.

Grannie, however, kept on probing. In a crafty manner she asked, "Wot woz the tune she woz a'playin' then, duckie?"

Grandad said (so that Grannie would not hear him), "Bloody *Alexander's Rag-Time Band*, I should think!"

We explained that as she was sitting on at least twenty keys at the same time, it sounded like nothing on Earth.

Grannie said sweetly, "An' wot woz Mr Fox a'doin' at the time, then?"

Grandad said (once again out of Grannie's earshot), "Wot the 'ell does yer think 'ee woz doin' – readin' the bloody *Encyclopedia Britannica*!

We said that by their respective attitudes, he appeared to be showing Miss Tester how to do the old-fashioned waltz.

Grandad snorted, "Wot! On the bloody organ! Sounds ter me as if she woz doin' more than an ol' fashioned waltz. More like leadin' 'im a merry ol' dance I'll be bound."

From that moment on, Grannie hopped back and forth

behind the curtains whenever Mr Fox passed by. We felt that there was more to the old-fashioned waltz than Grandad had said. And Grandad now seemed to hold Mr Fox in higher esteem than before. That was until the tomato episode.

CHAPTER SEVENTEEN

The Tomato Episode

"I knew I should never 'ave trusted the bugger!" said a steamed-up Grandad. "Now look what 'ee's done; made me the bloody laughin' stock of the village. I'll never be able ter 'old me 'ead up again! oh, the shame of it all," he wailed.

With that, he nipped into the shed for another glass of mild and bitter to drown his sorrows.

What had hurt him the most was the fact that Grannie had said, "It's yer own fault fer tryin' ter be too damn sharp. You've got yer just desserts. Don't 'spects no sympathy from me!" It had cut him to the quick.

Grannie had always backed him to the hilt on previous occasions. This time she had pulled the rug out from under him; after all, he had only tried to make the best of a disaster by doing what he thought to be right; surely she could see that.

Grannie could not. Being an opportunist was one thing, but telling lies to everyone in the village was another. As far as she was concerned, he had made his own bed, and he could lie on it, and, very appropriately, stew in his own juice!

It all came about, because Grandad struck upon a most novel ideal. It produced for him the most amazing crop of celery. It swept the board as the most outstanding vegetable at the village fête. Locals would come from far and wide, to stare with amazement at the size of it. His crowns had a girth of some twenty inches: they stood over two and a half feet high. Everyone – apart from Bryan and me – said that their flavour and texture were superb. They said that they were firm, crisp, and crunchy. They had the sweetness of freshly-picked chestnuts.

Bryan and I would not touch them with a barge-pole. We had seen Grandad, nipping through the darkness under cover of dusk, with the bucket from the little house up the garden. We had seen him shooting its contents into a trench dug for the purpose. We had heard him muttering in the darkness "Git a load of that me hearties! You'll be bloody pleased ter git out of that lot, I know." Not even under the threat of death would Bryan or I eat Grandad's celery. We would not even venture anywhere near the trench where it was growing.

When asked the secret of his celery, Grandad would, like the Artful Dodger, tap the side of his nose with his forefinger and say craftily, "The secret's in the night feed."

As far as we were concerned there was no secret about it, we knew what the night feed was, there was no way that we were going to die of anthrax to please Grandad.

It was the success of his celery, that prompted Grandad to take the course of action that he did. That, and the fact that Mr Fox had the most amazing contraption installed in his garden. The fact that Mr and Mrs Fox were socially our superiors, was emphasised by the fact that they had a cesspool and we had a bucket. But cesspools have their limitations, namely, that they have to be emptied. Mrs Fox found it embarrassing, not only for the men from the council to know the intimate details of her personal habits, but for the entire countryside, for half a mile in any direction, to know when this dreadful chore was being performed.

Mr Fox had his own pump installed, so that the disposal could be made silently, in relatively small lots, and buried in the two-acre field that adjoined his property.

A problem arose, however, when he had to find someone to wind the handle. This was about the size of an old-fashioned mangle and was on the side of a swan-necked, six-inch bore pipe, that came up from the cesspool below. The whole contraption made a clanking noise when operated. It was this that put anyone off from applying for the job. It was impressive when people were informed that one had a job working for the prestigious Mr Fox. It was spoiled somewhat, when you were seen winding the handle shifting something that completely spoiled the image.

Grandad, however, was not proud. He had a conference with his brother, Ern.

"Look wot it did fer the celery!" he said. "If we tried it out on the spuds, we'd be millionaires in a couple of years!"

Ern stood with his mouth open and agreed. "'Ow do we git it round 'ere then?" he asked.

Grandad, looking all benevolent said, "I'll git yer a high-speed barrer, you'll soon shift it."

Ern did not look too happy, "Why does it allus 'ave ter be me as shovel's poop," he said.

"'Cos yer allus does it so well," said Grandad. "Yer woz cut out fer it."

Grandad fitted the old wheel-barrow with a rubber tyre. He gave it a squirt of oil and said to Ern, "There you are, brother, that'll go like a Rolls-Royce, all you've got ter do is wind the 'andle, fill 'er up, and spread it on thick.

Ern did not look too happy.

He would have looked even unhappier, if he had known that Grandad had spoken with Mr Fox earlier in the day.

"Mr Fox," he said, lisping in an affected manner, as was his custom when addressing someone he considered above his social superior. "I've heard as 'ow you 'ent 'avin' no luck shiftin' yer poop."

Mr Fox looked at Grandad as if he were something the cat had brought in.

"If you are referring to the disposal of my sewage, Mr Packham," he said, "you are correct in your assumptions."

Grandad, adopting the air of a business tycoon said, "I'll take if orf yer 'ands fer sixpence a barrer-load."

Mr Fox sniffed and said, "Apart from the fact that I don't appear to have it on my hands, I would not like it to be made public that we have come to this arrangement."

Grandad tapped the side of his nose and said, "I'm a man of me word. We'll shift the poop fer a tanner a load, an' no one will be any the wiser!"

And so, in the soft sunshine of a new day, Grandad's brother, Ern, took his new 'Rolls Royce' the twenty yards from the top garden gate, to Mr Fox's mangle, and started winding.

All day he performed his task, staggering with fatigue as dusk began to fall. All in all Grandad, who stood with a pencil stub in his hand and an old notebook, calculated that his brother had shifted over forty barrow loads. For doing nothing, Grandad had earned one pound in a day;

a fortune, when a normal weeks wages would have been sixteen shillings. Grandad could not believe his luck.

After several more days, Ern said that the pump was running dry.

"I keeps a'windin' 'er," he said, "an all I does is puffs air! It 'ent a'comin' up as it ort ter."

Grandad and he studied points. "Christ!" said Grandad, "Don't it wiffle! Must 'ave bin down there years."

He reasoned that his crock of gold was running out. Mr and Mrs Fox had laid their last golden eggs so to speak.

Grandad collected his fee from Mr Fox. He said that he hoped that the arrangement had been satisfactory. Any time that he wanted the job repeated, he said, he would be willing to oblige. Mr Fox did not appear to want to talk about it.

Grandad's brother Ern then had the job of planting the potatoes. When he complained that he was the one who seemed to be doing all the work, Grandad, ever the silver tongue, said that as he was the only one who knew where he had shot Mr Fox's fertiliser, he was the only one who knew where to tread. It was logical, he said, that Ern should plant the potatoes.

Grandad's brother Ern planted half an acre of them. Grandad spent the proceeds of Ern's hard labour, with his cronies at the *Bo-Peep*.

It was obvious that something had gone wrong. Weeks before the potatoes were due to start sprouting, a green haze appeared over the potato patch. Grandad could not work out what it was. It was weeds of some kind, but Grandad did not now what. There were thousands of them. He and Ern studied the ever-increasing mass every day; they both drew a blank.

It was Walter Winchcombe who solved the problem. Leaning on the back gate one day, sucking a piece of straw, he said to Grandad, "Wot's the idea of growin' so many tomato plants then, Will?"

Grandad, not wishing to show himself up said, "They're a special variety Walter, when they gits bigger, I'm a goin' ter sell 'em around.

"Wot's so special about 'em, Will?" Walter asked.

"They're a prize variety, imported special fer Kentish growers," said Grandad.

"'Ow did yer gets yer 'ands on 'em, Will?" asked Walter.

Grandad swallowed hard. "Mr Fox gave 'em ter me," he said. He omitted to say *how* it was that Mr Fox had given them to him.

The seed had been sown in more ways than one. Walter high-tailed it down to the village, hot foot with the news that Ol' Will Packham had got a crop of special seed tomatoes that were going to shake the gardeners in the area to their roots.

Before long, Grandad had been approached by all the local tomato experts, who in various devious ways asked him if they could purchase some of his tomato plants. Purely out of interest, they said, just to see how they would turn out. Grandad obliged – at a price. Many a local grower winced at his charges. Tomato growers are a breed apart, like stamp collectors, they pay the earth. They all did, scuttling off to pot and re-pot; to nurture their offspring, to compete with rivals at the village fête later in the year.

Grandad sold many hundreds of Mr Fox's tomato plants. Once again the *Bo-Peep* had the pleasure of his business. Grannie was given her usual packet of Smith's Crisps (with the blue twist of salt inside) and a Brighton biscuit. Brother Ern was given some of the best tomato plants.

As the time of the fête approached, Grandad began to experience the first seeds of discontent. John Pritchard said that he had one plant four feet high, and thirty-six less than three inches. Trouble was looming.

One month before the fête, there were rumblings that Ol' Will Packham had sabotaged the tomato competition. At least half a dozen regulars in the *Five Bells*, and at least three in the *Bo-Peep*, were only speaking to Grandad through gritted teeth.

What Grandad had growing on the potato patch was the oddest collection of tomatoes ever seen. Apart from miniature ones the size of cherries, there were malformed monsters the size of cricket balls, smooth plum-shaped things more like plums than tomatoes, and brilliant yellow and green dappled ones. Grandad had no doubt that the plants that he had sold to the experts at such inflated prices, were exactly the same.

He, of course, put all the blame on Mr Fox. In public he said that Mr Fox must have got the seeds all mixed up. In order to keep the peace and his reputation intact, Grandad had to recompense his drinking partners by giving them their money back.

In private he said to Grannie, "Christ! Wot that silly ol' bugger gits up ter w'en 'ee buys tomatoes gawd knows! Never knowed such a bloody turn out! Talk about a mix-up. Why don't 'ee stick ter one bloody variety w'en 'ee eats 'em? Christ! What a mess!"

It was at this point that Grannie had shut him up by saying, "It's yer own fault fer tryin' ter be too damn sharp. You've got yer just desserts. Don't 'spect no sympathy from me!" She was quite right, of course, and he knew it. What particularly snarled him up, was that every penny that he had fiddled from Ern for carting Mr Fox's manure, had to be given back to bad-tempered tomato growers. It was rubbed in when Ern won the first prize for the tomatoes that Grandad had given him, at the village fête. The fact that everyone else had backed out was irrelevant. In Grandad's eyes it was the injustice of the thing.

His feelings were placated somewhat when he discovered that Ern had only won first prize in the novelty section. Evidently he had submitted four tomatoes that were shaped like doughnuts; complete with holes through their middles. Grandad felt even better, when he was told that apart from the rosette, the special prize in this category was a second-hand gramophone donated by the squire of the village, Mr Waring. Grandad felt that the irony of the situation was, that as his brother Ern was stone deaf, it was justice that was seen to be done!

The potato crop that followed the tomatoes was another matter. Something had affected them. They, too, were oddly shaped; they had a strange odour. At mealtimes, Bryan and I would enquire where they had come from. We knew where Grandad stored the crop from the various areas of the garden. If Grannie said, "from the store in the wash-house." we would decline her offer.

"Garn!" she would say, "they's the bestest 'taters ever. There 'ent nuffink wrong wiv 'em. They 'ent even got no wire-worm in!"

"No," we would mutter, "We're not surprised. There's not a wire-worm alive that would even stay in *that* potato patch, let alone live in it!"

Although Mr Fox had gone up in Grandad's estimation by teaching Miss Tester how to do the old-fashioned waltz, he sadly took a nose-dive over the episode of the tomatoes. "Any man," he moaned, "who can't make up 'is mind what bloody tomatoes ter eat, ent ter be bloody-well trusted! Bloody top me!" he said, "I wonders what the 'ell 'ee gits up ter, when 'ee eats apples? Christ knows what comes out the other end!"

CHAPTER EIGHTEEN

The 'unchback

Grannie had a dread of anything abnormal. Indian traders who visited from time to time, plying their wares from massive suitcases, bulging at the seams; with handles re-inforced with yards of string, were treated like lepers. Grannie would keep them well away from the back door, and shout at them at the top of her voice. Anyone cross-eyed, or with even a cast in one eye, would be avoided at all costs. Poor Freddy Gregory with his club foot was looked at sideways.

Imagine the situation them, when a little man of romany extraction, called at our back door selling greengrocery. Apart from the fact that we were completely self-sufficient in vegetables, we already purchased the odd thing or two from the donkey and cart of Arthur Checksfield.

It had all come about because Grannie had admired some extraordinary parsnips being prepared for lunch by her old friend, Gertie Dunmall. Miss Dunmall had no garden of her own to speak of. Grannie asked her where she had got them from.

Miss Dunmall replied "From 'Nobags', of course."

On enquiring who 'Nobags' was, Grannie was told that he was a little old man who lived in a ramshackle wooden shack situated half-way along Back Hill. This was the prettiest of bridle paths. It ran to the left, from the bottom of Well Hill, as far as the *Kent Hounds* public house. Sadly, it appears to be closed now. At one time it was a favourite walk on a Sunday morning. To go the half mile past the spring tap at the start of the hill, on up past Wen Wood and its famous pond, up and down through glades of bluebells, and to emerge at a quaint little pub for a glass of cider, was a glorious memory never to be forgotten.

It would appear that this old gentleman, called 'Nobags,' in order to make ends meet, had decided to grow his own vegetables and to start a green-grocery round. As a means of transport he constructed a trailer that was pulled behind his bicycle. It was this that he pedalled around the area plying his wares. At Grannie's instigation, Gertie Dunmall had sent him round, for her to have a look at his produce. The name 'Nobags' intrigued Grannie, who wanted to know what it was all about.

So it was, that 'Nobags' arrived at our house on a Saturday morning, all set to sell Grannie some of his parsnips.

What Grannie did not know, however, was that he was not held in very high esteem by the people of the village. He was also particularly deformed as well.

There are hunchbacks – and hunchbacks. According to Grandad, who was prone to exaggerate, he was so bent that although everything was upside-down, he could see backwards between his legs when he walked. Grandad also said that "when 'ee dies, 'ee woz so bloody crooked they would ave ter screw 'im inter the ground!" He added, "And I 'ent talkin' about 'is bloody bent back, either!"

Grannie saw this twisted little man coming up the path

by the side of the cottage. She shot upstairs as fast as her legs would carry her.

"Clear orf!" she cried from the safety of an upstairs window. "I 'ent in!"

"I've got sum lovely parsnips, Ellie," called 'Nobags'

"Don't yer Ellie me!" shouted Grannie. "I 'ent in ter-day, an' wot's more I don't want none."

"I'll leave 'em on the step then," said 'Nobags'.

"What fer?" said Grannie.

"'Cos I 'ent got no bags!" said 'Nobags'.

"Is that why they calls yer 'Nobags' then?" said Grannie, unable to contain her curiosity.

"Yus!" said 'Nobags', "It's 'cos I 'ent never got no bags."

"Call next week fer yer money!" said Grannie.

'Nobags' went on his way, up the garden and along Hollybush Lane. He stopped at the end of the lane, at a bank known as Greenels Een, to admire the evening primroses that grew there. After resting a while, he went on his way, to call on Lettie Smith. He sold her some magnificent Brussels sprouts. The odd thing was, that he never had Brussels sprouts in his trailer when he called on Grannie. After leaving Lettie Smith he called on Albert Blott. He sold him two pounds of new potatoes – freshly dug, straight out of the ground – he said. He never had any new potatoes in his trailer when he called on Lettie Smith. And so it went on. 'Nobags' had a constant supply of fresh vegetables that he never had before, at each new customer he called on. It was a mystery indeed.

It was years later, when comparing notes with old contemporaries, that the puzzle was solved. It would seem that 'Nobags' stole whatever vegetables he could lay his hands on, from the garden of the customer he had just left. He then sold these to the next customer on his round. It was simplicity itself. He never actually grew anything at all, just nicked the odd thing when leaving!

Grandad spotted the Brussels sprouts missing from the top of the garden, but assumed that Grannie had picked them. He moaned that it would make life easier if she had stuck to the rows. Grannie did not know what he was talking about. Similarly, Harry Smith noticed some new potatoes missing from the bottom end of his four-acre field that bordered the lane. He assumed that old 'Chicken' Smith, who worked for him on occasions, had helped himself – as Harry had told him to – on his way home. The last thing that Harry would have done, would have been to have asked the old man about it; that would have cast doubts on his honesty. Harry forgot about the incident; but wondered, when it seemed to become a regular event.

'Nobags' also did a roaring trade in Chelsfield village. He would cut across the fields from Albert Blott's place, gathering produce as hard as he could go, from either side of the footpath.

Several times, Sergeant Carver frisked him, and searched the old pram that 'Nobags' had converted into a trailer; each time he drew a blank. It seemed odd to the Sergeant that 'Nobags' trailer had a bottomless supply of vegetables. The truth of the matter was, that his supply of vegetables was indeed, bottomless.

His pram, as all mothers will know, had a storage area under the base. Whilst he had a few odd bits and pieces in full view above, concealed underneath, was a veritable Covent Garden of stolen produce. It was quite possible for him to get 10 lbs of new potatoes, 10 lbs of Brussels sprouts, 8 lbs of parsnips and a bunch of daffodils, all packed away in this secret compartment, without anyone suspecting a thing.

They watched him like a hawk in Neal's Stores, but the quickness of the hand deceived the eye. He would always order a can of paraffin and a bag of aniseed balls. One of the old girls would go out the back to get the paraffin, the other would have to get the step ladder to reach the aniseed balls on the top shelf. He would smugly go out with both pockets bulging!

'Nobags' had been banned at one time or another from all the public houses in the area. The *Bo-Peep*, the *Five Bells*, the *Rock and Fountain*, and the *Kent Hounds*. It was nearly always for the same reason; he smelled awful. John Pritchard said that apart from the fact that the very sight of him put the customers off, when the weather became hot, he nearly closed the pub down. Mrs Wright in the *Rock and Fountain* said that providing he used the bottom room, the bar furthest away from all the others, it was almost bearable. Apart from that she said, she was worried at what she might catch. Bert Parks at the *Five Bells* would not tolerate him at any price, and at the *Kent Hounds*, providing he used the bridle way, and came in by the back entrance so that no else would see him, he was allowed in for one drink only.

It will be gathered from this, that 'Nobags' had a problem. I suppose, that taking all things into account, he was the most unpopular character in the village. Without exception, he was disliked by everyone.

It was obvious, by his physical deformity, that he was not going to make old bones. It was obvious, too, by his standards of physical cleanliness, that in the passing of time, he was going to catch something or other that would cause him problems. And so it was.

Grannie, not wishing to get too close, was holding her

customary conversation with 'Nobags' from the upstairs bedroom window. He had remarked to Grannie that he did not feel too well. He said that he felt that the problem was his teeth.

Grannie said, "I don't know 'ow that s'posed ter be. Yer 'ent got none!"

'Nobags' said, "I 'ave! Yer jest 'ent never seen me a'wearin' on 'em."

When Grannie asked him why he never wore them he replied "'Cos they 'urts; they don't fit none too good. I've tried and I don't git on wiv 'em!"

He fumbled deep in his jacket pocket. With a flourish he pulled out the most disreputable-looking denture. This was stained in the most awful way. It was covered with whatever it was that contaminated the bottom of his jacket pocket. Grannie studied it from afar with the air of a professional.

"I'd take it back ter yer dentist," she said, "an' git 'im ter sort it out!"

"'Ent never bin ter no dentist," said 'Nobags'.

"Yer must 'ave," said Grannie. "'Ow else did yer git it?"

"Did a swop wiv' ol' Tommy Lee fer a bike tyre," said 'Nobags'.

Grandad appeared at the front gate and joined in. "Heard tell Tommy found 'em at the bottom of the hill when the pub turned out." he said.

"That's wot 'ee said," 'Nobags' confirmed.

"They'll never fit in a month of Sundays," Grandad said, "They woz made fer some other bugger!"

"Teeth is teeth!" said 'Nobags'. "Wot's good fer one is good fer all."

"Bloody top-me!" said Grandad. "Yer is eatin' yer

grub wiv someone else's bloody teeth. Christ knows wot you'll catch!"

"Never did 'im no 'arm," said 'Nobags'.

"'Ow would you know?" said Grandad, adding, "Do yer know 'im, then?"

"No," said 'Nobags', "but I reckon a man wiv only 'arf 'is teeth ought ter be easy ter find!"

Grandad looked niggled and said, "I'd git the bloody dentist to look at 'em!"

Grannie looked disdainful and said, "I'd go ter the doctor if I was you!"

Like all country people, 'Nobags' was terrified of the doctor. Grannie became suspicious when he failed to appear on his usual day. After a meeting with Mrs Dunmall, they both went up to his cottage in Back Hill to see what had happened to him.

Grannie came back full of it. They could get no reply from banging his back door. Grannie hit the door with a gardening fork that was leaning against the wall, only to find that it was open. They enquired at the top of their voices if anyone was in. With trepidation they entered the premises and carried out a systematic search.

According to Grannie, apart from the place being a pig-sty, there did not appear to be anyone at home. They searched the place from top to bottom but found nothing.

Purely as an afterthought, Grannie opened the door to his outside toilet, and was met with a sight that caused her to have nightmares for the rest of her life. Sitting in state was 'Nobags'. He had been dead for at least three days. Grannie said he was as stiff as a poker.

Grandad said, with true respect for the dead, "Christ! After three days, I bet he didn't 'arf smell!"

Grannie looked pious and replied, "'ee didn't smell no different to what he always did."

"That adds up!" said Grandad, "Wot did yer do then?"

"Tucked 'im in wiv 'is eiderdown," said Grannie, "and put a new top-hat we found on 'is 'ead."

"Wot the 'ell did yer do that fer?" asked Grandad.

"There woz a a leak in the roof, an' it woz a'drippin' on 'im," Grannie replied, adding, "We told John Divine, 'ee's gorn ter git the police."

Jack (sometimes known as Johnnie) Divine, was the unofficial caretaker of Chelsfield village. He happened to be passing on his bicycle at the time. On being informed that it looked as if 'Nobags' had departed to pastures new, he pedalled off as fast as his feet would go, to inform Sergeant Carver of the situation, and to get things organised with the vicar.

Unfortunately – because Grannie had not told him – he did not advise Sergeant Carver of the actual resting place of the top-hatted corpse. Consequently, when the trusty Sergeant arrived, it appeared that someone else had already done the collecting. Sergeant Carver went home and ate a hearty meal, prior to having a snore-up for the rest of the evening.

At nine o'clock that night, the vicar, the Reverend Mackay, arrived at Sergeant Carver's home in a state of panic. Everyone was looking for Mr 'Nobags', it appeared that he had gone missing. Would the Sergeant please go and have another look? he said.

Sergeant Carver was not happy. It was his night off. He did not fancy prowling around a derelict old shack in the dead of night, particularly when it was looking for a dirty old man whom he had never liked anyway. He was sure that they were wrong and that he had already been taken away. He found that the battery in his torch had expired, so, taking a hurricane lamp, he plodded into the night, bent on a bad-tempered errand which he knew would be useless, and for which he had no enthusiasm.

Sergeant Carver, to make his task more bearable, stopped at the back door of the *Rock and Fountain* for a free snifter. Not in the best of interests, he consumed far more than he should have done. He went on his way, feeling considerably happier than he had been before, glowing with a goodwill that had not been there earlier.

At the old shack he found, as he knew he would, the same situation as before. It felt eerie by the light of the hurricane lamp. Sergeant Carver felt jumpy.

It did not take too long for the sergeant to convince himself that he was on a fool's errand, and to terminate his search. It was then that something happened, that set in motion a train of events that had even stranger consequences.

Sergeant Carver had consumed three pints of stout in his brief sojourn at the *Rock and Fountain*. It is said that the capacity of the human bladder is one pint. It was this that caused the problem.

Sergeant Carver was not a young man, affairs of the bladder would suddenly announce themselves without warning. He found himself in such a predicament. He was at bursting point, the outside toilet was facing him; he pulled the door open and promptly wet himself!

In the ghostly half-light of the hurricane lamp, sat this awful apparition. It was wrapped in an eiderdown and was wearing a shiny top-hat. As the flame of his lamp flickered, the old man seemed to move his head, a half-smile played about his face. He even grimaced. Water dripped off his nose. "Christ!' said the sergeant, and fell backwards in the mud.

Hastily scrambling up, he ran as far as the *Kent Hounds*, where he asked to use their telephone. The landlord remarked that he looked as if he had seen a ghost. Sergeant Carver said that he bloody-well had!

He telephoned the ambulance service at Farnborough hospital and broke the good tidings to them. They (who only three weeks before had attended to Annie Evans with a broken toe) were none too keen to attend to an incident in the same place that had given them so much trouble before. They had found out the hard way, that there was no room to turn an ambulance round in Back Hill. They had to carry Annie Evans two-hundred yards up this muddy track on a stretcher. She rocked the scales at 14 stone. It was a task they would never forget. They made all the excuses available. In the end they said they would attend the scene, providing Sergeant Carver met them half-way. It was decided that the meeting would be at 10.30 pm – with the deceased – at the junction of Back Hill and Well Hill.

Sergeant Carver was then faced with the unenviable task of moving the corpse down 400 yards of unmade bridle path, in the dark, with no illumination of any kind. Admittedly there was the hurricane lamp, but when faced with a corpse, as stiff as a poker in a sitting position, the task of carrying this burden *and* a hurricane lamp, was virtually impossible.

Necessity, however, is the mother of invention. The trusty sergeant saw the answer to his problem leaning against a tree in the garden. It was the perambulator that had been converted to a trailer and fixed to the back of an ancient bicycle.

It was alcohol that provided the courage. Heaving the top-hatted figure over his shoulder, like a sack of coal, Sergeant Carver wedged it in the pram, facing backwards. All in the course of conforming with the Road Traffic Act, 1924, a rear light of some kind was necessary. This was achieved by clamping the hurricane lamp between the rigid knees of the corpse. The shiny silk top-hat completed the picture.

Sergeant Carver pedalled off into the night; his ghostly passenger rocking back and forth in the pram at the back, lighted by the flickering light of a ghostly oil lamp.

The ambulance men nearly had another casualty that night. Annie Evans was retiring for the night, and as was her custom, was drawing her bedroom curtains before getting into bed. Looking into the darkness of a pitch-black night, she saw a terrifying apparition gliding past in utter silence. She said afterwards, getting her times confused, that at the time that 'Nobags' had died, she actually saw his ghost floating by in the night. She said he was standing up, waving a ghostly light, rocking back and forth in a black chariot. She added that he was wearing a silk topper with ribbons streaming out behind!

Annie staggered back holding her throat and fell on the bed. She had screamed to her husband, Bill, who was locking up for the night. "Bill, come quick! The Devil's a'ridin' by. I 'ent ready ter go yet! Gawd 'elp us!"

Bill Evans revived her with a shot of whisky (kept purely for medicinal purposes). In short, he revived her with several more. Annie said that without doubt he saved her life. She vowed that she would never look out of that window again in the dark. "Fer fear of seein' 'im agin!" she said.

Sergeant Carver reached the junction of Well Hill and Back Hill, a few minutes before the ambulance arrived. This caused a minor problem. Two of the locals from the *Rock and Fountain*, staggering home with their caps on sideways singing *Nelly Dean*, met the Sergeant waiting with his ghostly hearse at the bottom of the hill.

"Wot's this 'ere, Sergeant Carver." slurred one. "Guy Fawkes night!"

The other said "Don't think much of yer bleedin' guy!"

They both bent over the sitting corpse and had a look. "Christ!" said one, "That 'ent bleedin' Guy Fawkes, that's a bleedin' stiff!"

They were last seen; knees well-up and caps gone, running flat-out the direction of Chelsfield village.

Before too long the ambulance arrived. The crew, consisting of a rotund jovial driver, and a tall, thin, miserable attendant, surveyed the scene.

"That looks like a bleedin' corpse to me!" said the miserable one, we 'ain't supposed ter carry corpses!"

"How do you know?" said the fat one, adding, "We'll only find out when the doctor sees 'im.

"I 'ain't liftin' no corpse in ter the back." said the thin one, "More than my job's worth!"

"Come on then," said Sergeant Carver to the fat one, "I've got a home ter go ter. I 'ent got all bloody night. I'll give yer a lift up! With that, the trusty sergeant grabbed 'Nobags' by the feet, the fat one lifted him under the arms, and they swung him into the ambulance.

It was then that something happened, that contributed to an awful situation at Chelsfield Church a week later. Parts of the human body, even in its demise, still continue to function for a while afterwards.

The digestive system is one of these. Food continues to digest, and in the process produces the gases inherent in that digestion. These have to come out somewhere; and this is exactly what happened. As 'Nobags' landed with a thump in the back of the ambulance, he farted very loudly!

Sergeant Carver, shaken to his roots, looked at the thin, miserable attendant and said, "Christ! Is he dead?"

The miserable attendant, with a look of extreme distaste on his face said, "Bloody-well smells like it!"

Not looking happy, they slammed the door and drove off into the night.

CHAPTER NINETEEN

Chelsfield Church

I have, before anything else, to make an apology to the Vicar of Chelsfield Church. Allow me to explain.

When the county planners decided, in all their wisdom, to construct the Orpington by-pass in the mid 20s, apart from giving excellent access to Orpington, they also neatly removed Cheslfield Church from the rest of the village. In our time, the by-pass became the western boundary of old Chelsfield; we never ventured across it. Our places of worship became the chapel in the village, and the tiny church on Well Hill.

In time, this became the accepted practice. Whilst the upper crust of the village tried to assure their places in Heaven, by giving generously and singing loudly in their private pews on Sundays, the village people generally only attended church on high days and holidays.

To a degree this is still so. I would suspect that most of the present congregation are from the newer developments to the west of the by-pass, rather than from old Chelsfield village.

My ignorance, therefore, of church matters, can be put down to the fact that I only attended Chelsfield church for births, marriages, and deaths. It will also explain why I originally thought that the minister at the church was a Vicar named The Reverend John Vigo.

I blame Grannie and Grandad, and a gentleman who was cutting the grass in Chelsfield Churchyard for this mistake. Grannie and Grandad, because anyone to do with the church was referred to as a 'Vicar'. And the reason that I compounded the error, by promoting the vicar *almost* to the status of an eminent snooker player? Simply, that when I decided to write of the great compassion shown to me by the minister at my mother's funeral, I asked a kind soul who was cutting the grass in the churchyard, for the name of the vicar. He told me his name was John Vigo.

We were consequently brought up to believe that vicars were the only representatives of the church in Chelsfield. Everyone in the hamlet of Maypole and the village of Chelsfield thought the same.

I must admit to a lack of knowledge of the hierarchy in the church. I do not know if a rector is superior to a vicar, or a canon to a bishop, or even if a bishop is above an arch-bishop. I blame Grannie and Grandad entirely for this omission in our religious instruction. I do not, however, feel that any of us are the worse because of it.

I understand that the minister in charge at St Martin of Tours, Chelsfield, is indeed the Reverend Leslie Virgo. He is a canon of Rochester, and Rector of Chelsfield. It is to him that I wish to tender my humble and most sincere apologies. I trust that he will be kind, and not condemn me to Hell and damnation for eternity.

Chelsfield Church is beautiful. It is a picture postcard. It sits in a place of tranquillity and lets the rest of the world speed by. Give or take a few years, it is not far short of a thousand years old. It has seen time come and go; it has rocked to the roar of anti-aircraft guns and German bombs. Through it all, it flies the flag of old Chelsfield village; it exemplifies a past life that once existed in Kent. Its name has mixed blessings. Grandad did not like the French. "Don't trust them bloody Frogs!" he would say, "they'll 'ave yer as soon as look at yer!" The present union with Europe could lead to an influx of French tourists. Mixed blessings indeed! I suppose that the lambs of the Lord are many!

It would seem that for the Church at Chelsfield to be mentioned in the Textus Roffensis (a list of Churches compiled by Bishop Ernulf of the Rochester Diocese in 1122), that the origins of the actual church, must have been prior to that date. Various other additions were made in the eleventh, fifteenth, and seventeenth centuries.

Chelsfields greatest claim to fame, is that it was home to a Lord Mayor of London. A memorial to *Brass Crosby, Lord Mayor of London*, is displayed in the church and confirms this fact.

The origin of the name of Chelsfield Church, *Saint Martin of Tours*, seems to be one of confusion. There were obviously communication problems at some time in the past. The original dedication was to a Saint Martin of Tours, of *Hasted*, in Ireland. It would also seem, that in 1659, Chelsfield Church was known as the Church of Saint James. Even in 1913, records refer to the name as being that of Saint Mary. So we have at Chelsfield a church that is named after one in Ireland, that was dedicated to a Saint Martin, of the city of Tours in France.

It is a pity that custom was not followed, and the name of Saint Mary established in common with those of earlier parish churches. Chelsfield Church would then clearly represent its own village, and not a city in France with which it has had no connection.

A jumble also seems to exist in Chelsfields claim to Brass Crosby. He was born in Stockton-on-Tees, lived in

London, and represented Honiton (in Devon) in Parliament. He is alleged to have resided in Chelsfield, but I know not where. He has two claims to fame. He was locked up in the Tower for defying Parliament, and became president of the largest lunatic asylum in London. Perhaps the two events were connected.

The history of Chelsfield Church is well documented. However, it is the undocumented trivialities of my time, the last fifty years, which though not particularly religious I find interesting. Simple things, like the fact that the first main tomb, a monolith of a monument, inside the church gate, erected to the Waring family, has a series of marks spaced out at six inch intervals, surrounding the base. The Waring family were one of the main supporters of the church. Mr Waring was the squire of the village. They were one of the landed families who contributed most to the church funds. Doubtless the reason for the prime position of the family tomb.

Although it is an irrelevance, and of no particular interest to anyone, for the sake of posterity and the hypocrisy of man, it must be recorded, that these marks are all that remain, of a magnificent set of railings that were removed during the war, to make bombs with which to kill Germans! How times have changed.

It is the same tomb, that in my mother's time, carried the challenge that if you ran round it ten times, at the end of the tenth time, the Devil himself would appear.

My mother has said, that on many occasions the young bloods at the village school have run round the tomb nine times, indeed even as many as nine-and-a-half times, but if, on tip-toe, with nerves stretched to breaking point, a gust of wind should blow through the avenue of trees that guard the approach to the church, the result would be a mad scramble to get out through the gate of the churchyard, for all the world as if 'Old Nick' himself were hard on their heels. My mother knew of no one who actually completed ten laps.

There was another artefact in Chelsfield Church that scared us half to death. This stood at the back of the church, at the opposite end to the altar.

It was a sinister, hearse-like cart, painted with shiny, black lacquer.

It had four large wheels, all of the same diameter, with eight spokes to each wheel. These were fine and elegant with thin, solid-rubber tyres. There was a wooden handle on a shaft meant for pulling. The body of the cart was a box, slightly larger than coffin-size, with sides that let down. These too, were painted in the same gloss black lacquer.

What made the whole thing more terrifying, was the dark-red velvet cloth with which it was draped. This hung down almost to the floor. It had a huge, golden cross embroidered on its uppermost side. Without doubt it covered the body reclining underneath.

As with the Waring tomb, it fascinated the village boys. Those of us who had joined the choir to get into the cricket team, would give it a wide berth when arriving for choir practice. As far as we were concerned, it stood in foreboding silence, containing the latest cadaver bound for the graveyard.

However, with the passage of time, one becomes used to the company of dead bodies. It was not too long before speculation was made as to whether there was actually a body laying there. It was decided to investigate. We arrived early for choir practice the following Tuesday. The honour of deciding who was going to uncover the resident corpse was decided by the simple process of choosing the one who bragged the loudest. Charlie Wickenden was designated for the job.

We stood with bated breath as Charlie approached the hearse. His feet seemed glued to the floor; he did not seem to be too keen on the job that he had shouted so much about.

"Go on then!" we whispered, "Wot yer 'angin' about fer?"

Charlie was walking on pins, "Give us time, then!" he said. "There 'ent nuffink to worry about."

He was approaching the hearse at the rate of one step a minute. It sounded as if he was trying to reassure himself.

"Get on wiv it!" we said, delighted at the fact that he was the one on the spot and not us, "We'll be 'ere all night."

Charlie was now within three feet of unmasking the horror to come. He was visibly shaking. Stretching a quivering hand out, he tentatively touched the red velvet cloth.

"There you are!" he said, "there 'ent nuffink in there!"

"Well go on," we hissed, "pull it orf."

Charlie once again stretched out his hand. Braver now, he got hold of the tasselled edge. As his wobbling hand began to take the strain the cloth began to stretch. With a sound like the clap of doom, the church door slammed with a bang that shook the church.

One would never have thought it possible for six boys to get out through the doorway of Chelsfield Church in the time that they did. Charlie, because he was the furthest from the door, was at the back. Those at the front could hear him shouting . . .

"Git out the bloody way! I'm sorry, God, I didn't mean no 'arm,!" This added to the panic of those in front, and

Plate 25: The wedding of Little Nell and Jim. The top-hat originally came from Tommy Lee

Plate 26: Little Nell with her first love, Toby Jefferys

Plate 27: Gracie Mason (Aunt Minnie's daughter from Hampton, who played dominoes on the settee with Mr Allen) Little Nell, Trimmer, and Jim

Plate 28: The dear people who started it all, Grandad and Grannie

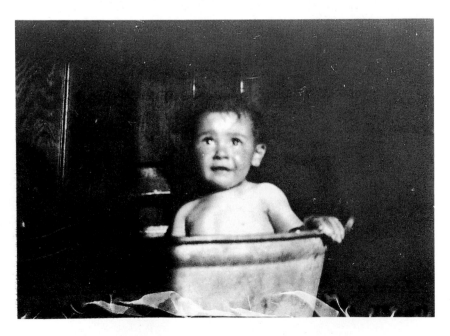

Plate 29: Friday night was bath night. The author, aged four, in a tin bath by the fire

Plate 30: Bryan, aged five. A school photograph

Plate 31: Chelsfield Primary School

Plate 32: St Martin of Tours. Left: *The Vestry partition that concealed Grandad.* Centre: *The Pulpit where the Reverend Mackay preached.* Right: *The resting place of 'Nobags' coffin*

Plate 33: The Wickenden Children from 'Crosshall'. Back: *Charlie and Frank*. Centre: *Vera*. Front: *Margery, Stanley, Eileen*

Plate 34: Joan Stevens: A beauty if ever there was one

also confirmed that even though Charlie Wickenden was braver than the rest, when it came to the crunch and the chips were down, he did not believe a word he said!

While I cannot vouch for the authenticity of this story, it has a similarity to the previous tale. It was repeated many times by Grandad; the facts all seem to fit. There are other aspects that seem to confirm its truth. The dates are right; Grandad's affinity with the reverend Mackay; and it was obvious that they shared a confidence.

According to various informants, it had to do with the death of either 'Arry, George, or Alf, Edwards. These were the alleged names of 'Nobags'. The year was 1936. The Reverend Mackay, all to do with eventually taking over at Chelsfield Church, was having the odd trial run or two.

Prior to his own investiture in 1938, he was becoming involved with church affairs to the extent of assisting the Rector incumbent, with various functions. Funerals were one of these. Thus it was, that the Reverend Mackay played 'hunt the corpse' with Sergeant Carver, at the time of the demise of 'Nobags' (who, for ease of reference, we will call 'Arry), on the 21st of May, 1936. This is not in doubt; the 21st May is my own date of birth. On the 20th of May, Grannie and Grandad held a conference to decide who was going to attend the funeral at Chelsfield Church. Because Grannie had this thing about physical defects, and hunchbacks in particular, it was decided that Grandad would attend.

Sergeant Carver gave him a black top-hat for the funeral. This had been amongst the personal effects of the deceased, returned to the sergeant by the ambulance service for passing to the next of kin. As there were no apparent next of kin, and the sergeant was sick to death of the sight of it, he reasoned that Grandad could make better use of it than he could. It turned out to be a collapsible one which hung around the old place for many years. It was regularly used for 'charades' at Christmas time!

Grandad looked well turned out on the day of the funeral; at least Grannie thought he did. She had managed to find some grey trousers with black stripes, and produced a pair of spats that had belonged to Mr Fox. These did not go well with brown golfing shoes, but they were all Grandad had. Grannie said the spats would cover the white tongue that hung over the laces. His jacket was a problem. Grannie got over this by borrowing a black frock-coat from Mrs Swift (our next-door neighbour), that had belonged to her husband who had passed away ten years before.

The whole effect must have been convincing. At the church, the undertaker who was conducting the funeral had a dust-up with Grandad. He thought that Grandad was another undertaker, attempting to poach his business. He apparently came up to Grandad in a most aggressive way and said, "wot's your bloody game, then?"

Grandad had stopped for a snifter at the *Five Bells*, and was full of Dutch courage. "Wot's me game is me own business!" he said, full of fight, "Want ter make somethin' out of it?"

The undertaker and Grandad stood very close. "I've met your bleedin kind afore," he said. "You city slickers wiv yer shiny silk 'ats. "Fink yer kin cum dahn 'ere and take me livin' away! I'll kick yer dahn the bleedin' 'ole!"

Just when things were looking fraught, with Grandad not relishing the thought of spoiling his outfit by an undignified roll in the mud, the situation was defused by the Reverend Mackay.

Sensing that there was trouble in the camp, and not wishing his first interment to be a disaster, he tactfully intervened by pretending not to have heard. He said, "I don't believe you gentlemen have met!"

Smiling benignly at the undertaker he said "allow me to introduce William Packham, one of the stalwarts of the community; a great supporter of the church you know!"

The undertaker swallowed hard. He knew by Grandad's lack of religious fervour and the obvious abundance of alcoholic bravado, that this statement by the Minister was highly suspect. The attitude of the Reverend Mackay made him stop and think. He had a job to do after all, it would not be in his interest to upset the man who was going to be the new Rector of St Martins. With a sickly smile, he held out a limp hand. He said with the intonation of a minister chanting a psalm. "We bury the dead in all humility, the Lord giveth and taketh away."

Grandad, jumping about like a firecracker said, "Wot yer on about, yer jest sed yer was a'goin' ter kick me dahn the bleedin' 'ole!"

The Reverend Mackay, pouring oil on troubled waters said, "You must have got hold of the wrong end of the stick, Mr Packham, now shake Mr Unwin by the hand, and let us gather together in friendship to bury the unfortunate Mr Edwards."

They reluctantly shook hands, Grandad muttering, "I'd like ter chuck *YOU* dahn the bloody 'ole!"

It was an inkling that things were going to go wrong.

The coffin was deposited on two wooden trestles near to the altar. Because "Nobags' was the most disliked person in the parish, the mourners that had gathered for his send-off were remarkably few. Grandad took pride of place in the front pew.

Because it was a trial run, and the Reverend Mackay intended to make a name for himself, he conducted a service that will be remembered by all.

After the preliminaries, he began to speak at length about the deceased.

It was now that Reverend Mackay came into his own. It was a bible thumping service if ever there was one. He told the congregation what he thought of them. He said that no one in the village had ever considered the cross that Harold Edwards had to bear. It was bad enough being deformed, without everyone being so unkind to him. How much nicer it would have been he said, if the people of the village had practised the teaching of the holy scriptures and cared for this poor individual.

The Reverend Mackay spoke for the best part of half an hour, extolling the virtues of 'Nobags' and castigating the congregation for their awful treatment of him whilst he was alive.

It was at the end of this sermon that the Reverend Mackay asked the congregation to kneel in prayer.

It was also at this point that something else happened. It caused Grandad and the Reverend Mackay to think deeply about the life hereafter.

In the moment of silence before the minister began to pray, when all was still and a pin could have been heard to drop, a barely perceptible squeak seemed to come from within the coffin containing Harold Edwards.

Probably because of a combination of rumours; the spectre of the phantom 'Nobags' in the dead of night, gliding past Annie Evans cottage, the ghastly puff of wind, that caught Sergeant Carver by surprise as the old man was being lifted into the ambulance. These, when added to Grannie's superstition concerning hunchbacks in particular, resulted in apprehensive mutterings amongst the village folk. There was something odd about the death of 'Nobags' they said.

Bearing this situation in mind, it will come as no surprise, that the whole congregation stood rooted to the spot. The Reverend Mackay had his mouth open, no sound coming out, gulping like a goldfish.

Grandad, who was standing next to the coffin and sharper than most, walked quickly to the other end of the pew and picked up a collection box. He said afterwards that this was purely an involuntary action. He said that he did not know why he did it. The next event proved the sense of his action, it should have made for a quick get-away. Sadly, it did not. The whole coffin, standing completely on its own, began to move. It was a gentle movement at first, it came from the end where the head of the deceased would have been, it would best be described as a judder. Nobody moved. The atmosphere could have been cut with a knife. The coffin shook much harder.

It was Grandad that started the riot. "Christ!" he said, in the most God-fearing manner. "I'm orf!"

His move to the end of the pew nearest the door proved to be of no great help. The doorway was filled with the rest of the congregation trying to get out; everyone else had got there before him!

Grandad said that when fear lends a hand, it is incredible what can be achieved in a few seconds. Although it seemed like an eternity, everyone was out – except Grandad and the Reverend Mackay – in less than ten seconds. Grandad said that he could feel the Reverend Mackay climbing all over his back.

Grandad flew down the path from the church door, hotly pursuing the other mourners. The Reverend Mackay, in trying to get through a rapidly closing door, caught his flowing robes on the latch. Grandad heard him yelp in terror. "Christ! For God's sake help me somebody."

Barely pausing in his stride, Grandad shouted over his shoulder, "Wot's up, mate?"

And the Reverend Mackay, voice high-pitched with terror, screeched in a most ungodly way, "The horrible little sod's got me by the jacket!"

This was followed by a loud ripping, as a pocket became detached from his jacket, and the Reverend Mackay, appearing from the confines of the church porch, like a bullet from a gun.

He passed Grandad half-way down the avenue of trees that led to the lane. The rest of the mourners and the undertaker had gone. He and Grandad stood in embarrassed silence and pondered the situation.

"What do we do now, Mr Packham?" said a white-faced Reverend Mackay.

"Best lets git back, an' gits 'im out of the coffin, then," said Grandad.

So they carefully crept back, Grandad pushing the Reverend Mackay in front, until they came upon the ministers pocket hanging on the door latch.

"Don't look the 'and of the 'unchback ter me." said Grandad.

"Well, what were you running for then?" said the Reverend Mackay.

"I was following the others!" said Grandad.

Together they eased open the church door. Two frightened faces noted the coffin still on the trestles where it had been before.

"Wot the 'ell's goin' on, then!" said Grandad.

"It's the work of the Lord," intoned the Reverend Mackay.

"No it 'ent!" said a sharp-eyed Grandad. "It's the work of the bloody trestle!"

Grandad had noted that a cord that should have been holding the rear supporting trestle legs together, was missing. He also noted that the legs were now a foot wider apart than they should have been.

All cocky now, he went over to the coffin, and lifting it gently placed the trestle legs back where they should have been.

Looking at the Reverend Mackay, Grandad put a slight pressure on the coffin lid. A faint groan appeared to come from within the coffin. This was followed by a movement, as the rear legs of the trestle, with no cord to hold them, began to move apart in a jolting motion. It was this that had made the coffin move. It was this that had caused Grandad, the Reverend Mackay, and the entire congregation of St Martin of Tours, to break the sound barrier at the thought of Harold Edwards, the despised hunchback of Back Hill, coming alive, and returning to haunt them.

With the undertaker now gone, Grandad and the Reverend Mackay had the task of completing the burial. Grandad found a ladder, and in the dusk of a winter's afternoon, they loaded 'Nobags' on board.

They carried him to the open grave, but a problem arose when it came to lowering the coffin down the hole. There were no ropes to assist them with the task. Grandad solved the problem in a very practical way. He asked the Reverend Mackay if he had ever conducted a naval burial service? It transpired that he had. Grandad asked him to conduct the service. As the reverend got to the part where the body is consigned to the deep, Grandad up-ended the ladder, and shot 'Nobags' down the hole! The Reverend Mackay said that it was all very irregular, but very effective!

The whole episode was kept very quiet. The mourners and the undertaker did not want everyone to hear of their stupidity. The Reverend Mackay did not want his superior the Reverend Folliott-Bough, to hear of the mess he had made of the burial, and Grandad and the new Rector-to-be became friends for ever. Grandad always said, that anyone who was honest enough to express his feelings in the way that he did when he thought that the ghostly hunchback from Back Hill had him by the jacket pocket, was a man to be respected and a true man of God.

There was another occasion when the Reverend Mackay had reason to express his heartfelt thanks to Grandad Packham.

At the top end of the village, in a place where Bert Parks built a contentious house, once stood a flint-built house with an adjoining stable. It belonged to an old German gentleman known as Heinrich Sigismund Uhlrich. His origins were unknown. He was married to a local Chelsfield girl known as Sara Ann Morgan. Old Mr Uhlrich was something of an artist. He would be seen, with a battered straw hat and large white beard, sitting at his easel in the fields that surround the village, painting the most beautiful watercolour pictures.

Mr Uhlrich was something of a patriot to his native country. He made it known that although Germany was beaten in the 1914–18 war, they would win the next one. Although they lost the 1939–45 war, it would seem that as they now apparently rule Europe, they did actually win the peace. Old Mr Uhlrich was correct after all.

With the passage of time, Sara Uhlrich eventually became infirm. She passed away on the 15th August 1929 in a nursing home. Old Mr Uhlrich carried on in the old house, until the years caught up with him too. He became infirm and passed away on the 5th November 1937. It was the occasion of his funeral that caused the Reverend Mackay more problems.

It was decided by Sara Uhlrich's relatives that old Mr Uhlrich should be buried at Chelsfield. They duly notified the old gentleman's relatives in Germany, that the funeral would take place at St Martin of Tours in Chelsfield. They invited any of them that wished, to attend the funeral.

The problem arose when the Rector, the Reverend Mackay, was asked to officiate. This was no great problem – it was when he was asked to take part of the service in German, that the troubles began!

The Reverend Mackay was visiting Grannie and Grandad on a Tuesday afternoon. He was looking worried. Grandad could tell that the Rector was not his normal self. "Wot's bitin' yer, Vicar!" asked Grandad.

"My problem, Mr Packham," he said, "is that I have no command of the German language."

It was Grannie that put the cat among the pigeons. "That 'ent no problem, sir," she said. "Daddy speaks it likes a Germin!"

Grandad had been showing off with his home-made radio set. He had picked up Dortmund. Sitting listening intently, he kept repeating with wonder, "Christ, 'ark at that bloody lot!"

Everything seemed a jumble to Grannie. She asked Grandad what it was all about?

"Bloody simple!" he said. "'ear that! 'Ee's tellin' all Germiny the time."

"'Ow does yer know?" said Grannie.

"Easy!" boasted Grandad. "Sax un zen, is ten past six!" It's as plain as the nose on yer face."

"Kin yer speaks Germin then?" said Grannie.

"Course I bloody well can!" said Grandad. He was now in hot water up to the neck.

The Reverend Mackay seized on this opportunity like a drowning man grasping a straw. "Can you give me some instructions then, Mr Packham?" he asked.

It became obvious after a while that the Minister had no grasp of the German language. "NO!" Shouted Grandad. "It 'ent bloody Himmel! It's 'immel." And later, "Christ! NOT 'oly Walter, 'erlig wasser!'"

The three of them went into conference. Grannie decided that the best thing to do, would be to read the Lord's Prayer, half in English and half in German, that way she said, "they kin all 'ave a bit." Grandad should go to the service she said. He could stand concealed in the part of the vestry next to the pulpit, prompting as required, through the curtains, and behind the wooden bars that separated him from the Rector. Grandad did his best to translate the Lord's Prayer into German. Grandad's advice to the Rector on the day of the funeral was "ter mumble, so's ter confuse 'em a bit!"

Unlike the funeral of 'Arry Edwards, everything went according to plan. Mr Uhlrich's relatives arrived in the form of three huge men with shaven heads and walrus moustaches. They wore tiny green yodelling hats with feathers in the hat bands. Their wives, very fat with circular plaits over their ears, all wore robust walking boots.

Grandad had made a bit of a mess of the translation of

the Lord's Prayer. It was decided that he would whisper to the Rector the odd German word, for the Rector to substitute in the appropriate places.

The Lord's Prayer was to be the highlight of the proceedings. All went well until the Rector began the Lord's Prayer and Grandad did his translation bit!

The Rector began, "Our Father,"

Grandad whispered "Varter."

The Rector said "Farter."

"No!" hissed Grandad. "It 'ent Farter, it's Varter!"

The local village people began to titter. The Rector blushed scarlet, muttered his apologies, and carried on.

"Who art in Heaven,"

"Himmel!" Grandad said.

"I'm afraid that does not sound correct," said the Rector. "Who art in Himmel is definitely wrong."

"Try 'immel then!" said Grandad.

"Who art in 'immel," said the Rector with a smug look. "I'm sure you'll agree that's much better!"

Grandad looked narked.

The Rector continued, "Hallowed be thy name."

Grandad hissed "namen!"

Once again the Rector contradicted Grandad, "It can't possibly be 'namen', Mr Packham. Hallowed be they namen, is definitely wrong!"

Grandad felt niggled. "Well!" he said, "you 'ent exactly gittin' fings right. Since when 'as 'is name bin 'allo'ed? I was allus taught ter call 'im 'Our Lord' at Sunday School!

"All right," said the Rector, admitting defeat. Not wishing to be shown up in front of the German visitors he said, "Our Lord be they namen!"

He added, "They Kingdom come," and looked at Grandad.

Grandad, put on the spot, and not wishing to show his ignorance said, "Donner and blitzen!"

"Donner and blitzen!" said the Rector. The Germans looked amazed.

The Rector continued "Thy will be done, on Earth."

Grandad, all at sea now, said, "Gott mit uns!" (he had read this on a German military buckle in the National War Museum).

The Rector repeated "Got mit uns!". At least this fitted in. He carried on "as it is in Heaven."

Grandad said "Auf Weidersehen."

"It can't be!" said the Rector, "you said that Heaven was 'immel in the first line, it can't be 'of weedersain' in this one!"

"It bloody-well is!" said an embarrassed Grandad. It was now becoming obvious that his knowledge of the German language was nil. "Yer jest 'ent saying' it right, Vicar."

"If you say so then," said the Rector. He said, very loudly, "Auf Wiedersehen!"

All the Germans stood, clapped heartily, bowed stiffly, and went out.

"There you are," whispered Grandad. "They thought it was good!"

"Yes," said the Reverend Mackay (out of the side of his mouth), "they seemed to show their appreciation by their applause".

When the rest of the congregation had gone, Grandad and the Reverend Mackay congratulated themselves on a job well done.

"I think you can say, Mr Packham," said the Rector, "that although they all walked out half-way through the Lord's Prayer, your linguistic effort was considerable. A bit of a combined effort you might say!"

In the *Bo-Peep*, Grandad became unbearable with his command of German. Later, when he picked up Peking on his radio, Grannie said "kin yer speeks Chinese then Father?" Grandad replied emphatically, "No, I bloody well can't!"

CHAPTER TWENTY

The 'Black Sock Gang'

It is strange how facts come to light that solve past mysteries. I can remember sorting through the ruins of old Mr Uhlrich's house with Bryan. We found vast amounts of partly-burned German newspapers. These confirmed our suspicions that without doubt, old Mr Uhlrich had been a German spy!

The seeds were sown when we heard the family discussing how it was that Mr Uhlrich's house had been burned down. Dorrie said that it had been some of the village boys who had always suspected the old man of being a German spy. He was over 90 years of age, and the 1914–18 War had been over for twenty years. In a fit of misguided patriotism they had set fire to the house.

It would seem that after a long illness, Mr Uhlrich was taken ill, and ended up in the County Hospital at Maidstone. He was informed while in hospital that his house had been destroyed by fire. It was probably this that finished him off.

Fifty years later, I made contact with Alec, the eldest and the last of the Stevens boys (sadly, Syd died during the preparation of this book). These were three little boys who were taken in and brought up as part of the family by Grannie and Grandad. They were orphaned when their mother died in the Battersea area of London.

Homes were found for them, when their father was not able to work *and* look after them as well. Several things came out in the conversation. I enquired as to Alec's two brothers, Syd and Albert.

Alec corrected me. "You've got it wrong, Derek," he said. "There were seven of us! Apart from myself, Syd, and Albert, there was Harry, Bill, Len, and a sister, Alice."

It would seem that a Nurse Harris, who lived at St Mary Cray, placed children who were in difficult circumstances with various families in the area. Alec said that all his brothers lived locally. His sister, Alice, lived in Bournemouth. He said that his father visited them regularly at the old cottage. His visits were at three-weekly intervals and continued for many years. For no apparent reason they suddenly stopped. The boys never saw him again.

It was Alec that filled in the details on old Mr Uhlrich. We were discussing old Chelsfield village and the subject of the fire at Mr Uhlrich's house. I said that I understood that it was the work of misguided vandals in the village.

He said, "No, Derek, it was two gypsies who lived at St Mary Cray."

I asked him how it was that he knew this?

Quite casually he replied, "because I ran them over on the main road at Goddington!"

It transpired that Alec had taken the young lady (who was later to become his wife) home to her mother, Mrs Wright, who owned a cycle shop at St Mary Cray. It was an extremely foggy night. Alec had to wind up the windscreen of the old Morris Eight that he was driving, in order to see. At the part of Court Road that crosses Goddington Lane the fog was particularly thick. Alec suddenly felt two thuds as the car hit something. This was followed by shouting on either side of the car. He stopped and scrambled out to find two people laying injured, one on each side of the car. He said that they were kicking up a hell of a racket.

Running to a nearby house, he asked the householder to raise the police and an ambulance. He went back to try to assist the injured until help arrived. He noticed that the two men involved were of the Romany variety.

Within a short while the police and ambulance arrived. Alec noticed an odd thing about the two casualties. It was while they were being examined, prior to being put in the ambulance, that he noticed they both had black socks on.

While Alec was pondering this strange phenomenon, the police were engaged in other things. It would seem that these apparent vagrants were in possession of a number of expensive articles that clearly did not belong to them. Alec also noticed – as they were being lifted on to stretchers, that neither of them were actually wearing socks. What he had taken to be black socks was actually the colour of their feet.

The ambulance men diagnosed that one had a broken leg, and the other was badly bruised. They were taken to Orpington Hospital.

On being questioned by the police at the hospital, it transpired that they had robbed old Mr Uhlrich's house and set fire to the property to remove any evidence left that could have incriminated them.

There was another theft from what was left of old Mr Uhlrich's house. The only part left standing was a lean-to of flint construction that was part of the house. It contained a magnificent four-wheeled trap that was used on special occasions by Mr Uhlrich and his wife.

It was elegance itself. It had extremely thin wheels with narrow tyres, the seats were upholstered in the best leather, all armrests were covered with matching brown velvet. Any leather was burnished to a deep shine, and all fittings were of the best quality brass. It was completely undamaged and was a joy to behold. Someone else thought so too. It disappeared like magic after the fire – it was never seen again.

The three Stevens boys that had made *Yewtree House* their home, came from poor origins in London. Grannie and Grandad took them to their hearts. They became part of the family. Life in the Kentish countryside was completely different to anything they had known. They had food, and a way of life that they never dreamed existed. Grannie, true to form, fed them up on country fare – enormous lamb stews, thick with herbs and lentils, with dumplings as heavy as lead were the norm. Bacon puddings, six pounds in weight, loaded with sage and onions, and tied up in a pudding cloth, came glistening from the pot. Huge breakfasts of bacon and Charlie Strout's famous sausages, surmounting masses of bubble and squeak, crisp and brown, made them protest they could take no more, even though filled to bursting point and groaning with discomfort, it made men of them.

The first Christmas they spent in the old cottage, Grannie resolved to make a memorable one. What better Grandad said, for them to have an actual visit by Father Christmas himself.

On Christmas morning, Little Nell, dressed as Father Christmas, with a long, white beard, nipped out unseen by the front door, and crept around the lane, to appear at the gate at the top of the garden ringing a hand-bell. Grandad remarked to the three little boys, that he thought he could hear Father Christmas ringing his bell and coming down the garden path. The outcome was different to what the family expected. Three little pairs of eyes looked as if they were going to pop out of their heads. There was, as Grandad said, "a hell of a scamper to get behind Grannie's skirts." Albert shouted "tell 'im ter git out!" Syd said "I don't want yer bleedin' toys!" And Alec said "Bugger orf back ter yer sledge!" They had never seen Father Christmas before and obviously had no wish to see him again.

CHAPTER TWENTY-ONE
A Divine Happening

There was another fire at Chelsfield that caused problems. Sadly it was helped along by Bryan and me. It also caused a serious row between Jack Divine and his wife Vera. A hose was involved.

I have written of this fire before, but with the passing of time, other facts have come to light that were associated with the event, that should be recorded for posterity.

It is well known that Jack Divine was the unofficial caretaker of Chelsfield village. In later years he also seemed to take over the churchyard. I suppose that with a name like Divine this was inevitable. His motives were undoubtedly good, it was his attitude that people found irritating. He always seemed to bustle about in a hurry. Even if it was only to pick up a bus ticket on the pavement it was done as if it was the most important thing in the world. Should anyone stop their car in the village street, within seconds Jack would be there, asking them what their business was. If a bicycle was leaned against a fence, Jack could be heard bawling "Oi! Yer can't leave that there!" It was consequently very satisfying when we heard the outcome of our contribution to the village bonfire on 5th November 1947.

It all came about because in 1944 Bryan had found a container of German incendiary bombs that had hit the top of a beech tree in Shoreham Woods. There was a multitude of bombs scattered everywhere. We collected as many as we could carry in a sack, and carried them home on the cross-bar of my bicycle. Apart from the fact that they were superb to bargain with when haggling for souvenirs, they provided a constant source of entertainment. The detonators, when hit with a hammer, made a bang that made your ears ring. An explosive one (painted bright yellow with a red ring around it) caused the local Home Guard to turn out and my mother to think that there had been an air raid. We exploded it under a dipping tank in the woods. Bryan and I suffered concussion and ringing in the ears for four hours afterwards. The magnesium powder that they contained burned with a brilliant, blue light. It was quite possible, if you sprinkled the letters on the ground, to actually burn ones initials into a concrete path. The frightening thing was the casing. Once this got going it seemed to melt the actual soil. It was almost impossible to put out.

Imagine the situation, therefore, when we put the remaining two on the village bonfire that was built to celebrate Guy Fawkes night. All that Bryan and I knew was that we saw Chelsfield's 5th November bonfire from over three miles away. In truth, it lighted the heavens for miles around.

The story that emerged fifty years later, was that all the youth organisations – the Boy Scouts, Sea Scouts, Army, Navy and Air Cadets, Girl Guides, Brownies, and various church organisations, all gathered round the bonfire to sing hymns conducted by the vicar.

It would seem that as the fire began to generate heat, the crowd moved back. As the heat increased, the crowd moved back further still. When both bombs were really going everyone was packed against the far hedges of the recreation ground. The vicar had his sun-glasses on, and Jack Divine was in a state of near panic. He of course, was a big-gun when it came to being a warden. The safety of Chelsfield village was entrusted to him personally. He was Chief Warden, Head of the Fire Watchers, and the acknowledged expert on the use of the stirrup pump. When things began to get out of control, Jack Divine came into his own. He took charge.

Appearing in a white, steel helmet, with 'Chief Warden' emblazoned on the front. He made a thorough nuisance of himself by bawling to everyone to stand well back (this was completely academic, everyone was standing as far back as they could anyway). He rushed behind the cricket pavilion, and emerged with two sandbags. Standing thirty feet away he threw them on the fire. At least that was his intention, but twenty-eight pounds of sandbag thrown from thirty feet do not travel very far. They both hit the ground ten feet from where he was standing.

As the fire was now a raging inferno that the London fire Brigade would have had trouble putting out, Jack Divine resorted to the next plan of action. He screamed for his wife!

"Vera!" he shouted, like a fog-horn. "Git the bleedin' hose!"

Vera Divine was a sweet soul. She supported her husband to the hilt. She appeared in the darkness from her garden gate with a hose-pipe.

"Fix the end on the bleedin' cock!" bawled Jack.

Vera groped about on the ground trying to find the stop-cock. Jack, all belt and braces, now ready for action, shouted. "Stand back everyone, here I come!"

Adjusting his hat, and putting on a grim air of determination, he charged, with his end of the hose at the ready, full tilt towards the fire.

The crowd parted to let him through. The hose, as taut as a violin string, followed on behind.

Jack, head well down, bellowed, "Turn 'er on, Vera!"

Vera said in a barely audible voice, "I can't!"

Jack shouted "Why the 'ell not?"

Vera replied, in a voice quivering with emotion, "'Cos you're dragging me along on me arse, through the bleedin' mud!"

It would seem that Vera, groping about in the dark for the stop-cock. had stood in the middle of the coiled hosepipe. Jack, taking off at thirty miles per hour, had pulled her off her feet and dragged her for twenty yards through the mud. Vera was not happy. She called him a 'Prat!' (whatever that was). She said that she even had mud on her back, on the *inside* of her dress.

Even with Jack laying on the ground with the hose – bawling out for the water to be turned on – nothing happened. This was because Vera Divine had stormed off leaving them all to it. The Vicar could not find the stop-cock in the dark; it would have been difficult enough to find normally, but the fact that he had his sun-glasses on, made the task impossible. The whole thing turned into a farce. It was the only real 'dust-up' that Jack and Vera Divine had in fifty years of married bliss.

Despite the episode of the great fire, Jack Divine did not change his ways. He still interfered in all village affairs; he considered himself the custodian of the village. His heart was in the right place, however. All that he ever did, was with the best of intentions. His like will never be seen again.

When his wife passed away, Jack Divine could be

found on Summer evenings in the churchyard. He would be leaning on his rake, spending time with his dearly beloved. He, of course, took over the churchyard – that was his way. He found pleasure, spending time with the old people, those that he had spent his life with. Almost a Divine right one might say.

CHAPTER TWENTY-TWO

In the Money

An incident, typical of country life, involving Grannie and Grandad Packham at the old cottage, concerned Arthur Checksfield and his vegetable round.

A normal Saturday morning in the summer would consist of warm sunshine, all the doors and windows open, the dog snoring contentedly on the doormat. Everyone would be wandering aimlessly about their business with the odd chicken or two on the doorstep, getting in everyone's way worrying for corn. Normally the kettle, heavy with soot, would be singing merrily on the fire.

If it were mid-morning, Grandad would have come in from digging the potatoes. He would be sitting by the fire with legs spread out reading the *Picture Post*, or holding forth on the latest predictions in *Old Moore's Almanac*. His brother, Ern, would be sitting on the other side of the fire, poring over Gipsy Petralingo in the *People*, who Ern believed implicitly. They both argued constantly over their respective astrologers, insisting that each was right.

"Ol' Moore got the bleedin' weather wrong agin!" Ern would say.

Grandad would reply, "Your 'ent cum inter no bloody fortune, like that fiddlin' Gypo said yer would, either!"

On this particular morning, Grannie appeared from the darkness of her pantry looking bad-tempered. "The only one about 'ere makin' a fortune," she said, "is that damned Arthur Checksfield. I 'ent payin' 'is fancy prices no more. You kin answer the door w'en he comes a'knockin', 'ee's as big a fiddler as that damned ol' Petralingo!"

Grandad could see that Grannie was niggled. "Wot's up then, Mother?" he said.

Grannie had been to the village to do some shopping. She had paid her customary visit to Neal's Stores to buy odds and ends, and to stop to catch up on the village gossip.

The old girls in the shop were doing a cut and thrust job on Arthur Checksfield. He was taking their trade away they said, it was unfair because the only overheads he had were his donkey and cart. Grannie distinctly heard them say that when it came to money, he had piles!

Grannie had firm ideas about what was right and what was wrong. When an incident was told of a complete stranger, obviously a city gentleman, asking Arthur the way to Knockholt station, Arthur started his customary stuttering. His intentions were, to tell the traveller to turn right at the *Bo-Peep*. He got stuck on the 'B'. He stood for several minutes stuttering B-B-B-B-B.

The city gentleman impatiently said, "Hurry up man, I've got a train to catch!"

This cured Arthur's stutter immediately. "B-Bugger orf then!" he said.

The old girls in the shop gasped with horror. "What a dreadful way to treat a gentleman!" they said.

Grannie (although used to such language from Grandad) agreed with them. She was narked at Arthur Checksfield being in the money at her expense. "Someone ought to tell him about his prices," she said. Grannie decided it was a job for Grandad. When she got back to the old cottage she repeated the story. Grandad was to say that she was buying her goods elsewhere.

At eleven o'clock that morning, Arthur Checksfield stopped at the front gate and rang his bell. Grandad wandered down the front path to pass the time of day.

"Morning', Arthur." he said. "See you've got a new nappy on the donkey."

"Y-Y-Yus, Will," he said. "G-G-Gawd knows 'ow I kin a-f-f-fford it."

"I heard tell that you're in the money these days!" said Grandad, turning the conversation.

"O-O-Ow'd yer make that out then, W-W-W-Will?" asked Arthur.

"Accordin' ter Mother, you've got piles!" said Grandad

"S-S-So I 'ave, said Arthur. "B-B-But wot's that ter do wiv 'avin' money? More like 'avin' a load of nettles in me damn t-t-trousers!"

Out of sheer embarrassment, Grandad bought two pounds of parsnips. He appeared at the back door looking snarled up. "Christ!" he said. "Why the bloody 'ell do I listen ter Mother. Now I've gorn and bought 'is bloody parsnips. I've got the best part of two 'undred-weight in the bloody shed!"

Grannie came out of the pantry, wiping her hands on a dish-cloth. "Did yer tell 'im, Father?" she asked, looking keenly at him through a haze of cigarette smoke.

"No, I bloody-well didn't!" snapped Grandad. "He's as bloody broke as I am. Where yer gits these stories from I'm buggered if I know!"

"Them's gals at the shop sed 'ee 'ad piles," said Grannie humbly.

"So 'ee 'as," said Grandad. "Up his backside, not in his pocket!"

Grannie looked puzzled. "A funny place ter keep yer money," she said.

"'Ee don't keep 'is money there," said Grandad. "That's where 'ee keeps 'is piles!"

Slowly the realisation came to Grannie. She was venturing into pastures new. "Wot's piles then, Daddie?" she asked.

Grandad, ever the height of propriety said, "Varicose veins on the arse!"

"I only ever git's 'em on me legs!" said Grannie with a supercilious look. "'Ee must 'ave bin wicked ter gits 'em there!"

"Wicked 'ent nothin' ter do wiv it!" said Grandad. "Ern's got one or two, and 'ee 'ent wicked!"

Grannie looked a shade testy. "'Ee 'ent none too holy either!" she said, adding "'Ow der you know anyway?"

"'Cos 'ee said, it felt as if 'ee 'ad a bunch of 'olly up the back!" said Grandad.

"I 'ope 'ee 'ent got it from the tree by the top garden gate!" Grannie replied. "I was keepin' that fer the Christmas puddin'."

Grandad replied, "In that case, I don't want none!"

At that moment Brother Ern looked up from his newspaper; Grannie shouted "You keep away from that 'olly tree by the top gate!".

He sat with his mouth open and nodded.

Grandad said "It 'ent no good talkin', Mother. 'Ee don't know wot you're on about." He added silently, "I'm buggered if I know's either!"

Grannie summed it all up by saying that she *might* buy one or two things from Arthur Checksfield in the future, but she would make sure that he washed his hands before serving her.

The world in the old cottage would turn a few more

times. Dorrie would come looking for the 'Blue' bag that Grannie had put somewhere safe, but could not remember where. Little Nell would come in, complaining that it was always she that had to mow the lawn. Bryan and I, having had a huge breakfast in bed, would be reading comics and thinking of getting up. This would be in time for lunch, and to catch the 431 bus to Orpington. We would have a look around the shops before going to the *Commodore* cinema to see the latest Bob Hope and Bing Crosby film. We would get back to Grannie and Grandad at the old cottage in time for tea.

CHAPTER TWENTY-THREE

An Odd Situation

It was generally known in the village that Bert Parks preferred hob-nobbing with the gentry that graced the saloon bar of the *Five Bells*. He could be found – an exaggerated *mine host* – beaming benevolence and laughing too loudly at the jokes of his high-brow customers. It was a known fact that he would only serve in the public bar under sufferance.

Bert, however, faced a dilemma. He was extremely uncomfortable with a member of the community who, like most of the inhabitants of Chelsfield, was not strictly upper class. He was a strong personality known as Richard Sanderson. He was not particularly well known in the village prior to the beginning of the war. His main claim to fame at this time, was that he drank in the public bar of the *Five Bells*.

By a strange quirk of fate and a great deal of ability, Dick Sanderson emerged on the village scene in 1940, as a lieutenant in the Home Guard. He still insisted on using the public bar in the pub.

Bert Parks was now confused. As Grandad said, he did not know whether was was punched, bored, or countersunk. Here was an officer, albeit in the Home Guard, with whom he should be hob-nobbing. He put himself out of bounds by associating with the scruffs in the four-ale bar. Bert felt that his own attitude was excusable. Dick Sanderson was only in the Home Guard, and not the real army.

The cat was really put amongst the pigeons when Lieutenant Sanderson was called up, emerging in a very short while as Captain Dick Sanderson of the Suffolk Regiment.

In the public bar, Bert did not know whether to acknowledge his presence or to pretend that he was not there. It was a stand-off situation. They sized each other up like a pair of fighting cocks.

Captain Dick Sanderson (known as Captain 'Dickers' to his grand-children) took a wicked delight in putting Bert Parks on the hot seat. It was extremely difficult for Bert to socialise with a War Office Lieutenant in the saloon bar, when a fully-fledged Captain in a fighting regiment was mixing with the hob-nailed brigade in the public bar. On these occasions, Bert would force a grim smile. He would say through gritted teeth, "Good morning, Dick." One could tell that his smile caused him actual physical pain.

This went on for the duration of the war. Gradually a dislike built up between them.

When hostilities ceased (between Great Britain and Germany – not Bert Parks and Dick Sanderson!), it was obvious that Dick Sanderson was going places. He began a business in the village as a general builder. Before long there were vans and lorries with *Sanderson Brothers, Master Builders* emblazoned on their sides in the sign-writers best hand. Bert Parks nearly burst a blood vessel. He resented this upstart taking things over. Things began to get nasty between them.

It really was a war of attrition. They were evenly matched. The strings that Bert could pull with his high-level cronies in the saloon bar, were matched by the strings that Dick pulled with his contacts amongst his employees, and others who had no great liking for the wily Bert.

Whilst Dick would be informed by an employee that a tumbledown cottage had just fallen down, unless he moved quickly, Bert would find who the land belonged to, and put in a bid for it! To counteract this, Dick would apply for outline planning permission and raise the asking price. Bert would then have to increase his offer, and would end up by paying £1,000 more than he intended! When he had completed the deal, he would apply for planning permission, only to find that Dick Sanderson had made an objection, that the projected development did not conform to planning regulations. They fought tooth and nail. To this day there are odd plots of land in the area that belong to the descendants of Dick Sanderson that even *they* do not know about!

Events moved fast and furious. When Bert tried to covertly buy the piece of land that old Mr Uhlrich's house had occupied, Dick Sanderson had already set the wheels in motion. Bert, however, by a supreme bit of cunning and a tip-off from the planning officer, clinched the sale.

Dick screamed his head off and tore his hair out – all to no avail. He screamed even louder when he saw a red-brick building, completely out of character with the mellow houses in the high street, going up on the piece of land that directly overlooked his own property in the centre of the village.

Once again the protests flew backwards and forwards to the planning office. Once again Captain Sanderson tore his hair out. On this occasion, Bert Parks (and the planning officer) emerged triumphant. It was Dick Sanderson, however, that had the last laugh.

It was Sandersons the builders who were given the job of demolishing the wonderful old house that had been our family home for over three-hundred years. The story of its demolition brought great sadness to everyone in the area. Those who had bought about its demise will never be forgiven for this act of vandalism. Even when they had knocked the guts out of the old place, they could not break its back.

The timbers of its frame, made from oak beams taken from the sailing ships of the Thames Estuary, were impregnated with tar and salt and seasoned from many years at sea. They refused to break from the sledge-hammers of the demolishers. In the end, only by a steel hawser attached to the mighty elm trees on the far side of the lane, did they manage to winch it down.

Mr Saunders, one of Dick Sandersons employees, said with a great sadness, and eyes filled with tears, that the old house really did scream when the hawsers finally wreaked their destruction. It was very upsetting. He said that it 'hurt him inside'.

It was Mr Saunders who gave me the old front door key. He had found it still hanging from a beam in the pile of rubble. I have it in a safe place now. I suppose that one day, someone will throw it in a dustbin. They will be unaware of the history of that heavy, old key. They will never know the incredible tale of the three-hundred years of happiness that it kept locked behind it's front door.

It was these beams that enabled Dick Sanderson to level the score with Bert Parks.

Dick let it be known what superb timbers had come from the old house. He said that for a small consideration he would be prepared to sell them to any buyer that was interested. Old, seasoned oak, at that time was selling for £5 a cubic foot. Dick Sanderson dangled the bait by saying that any buyer could take it away for £2.10s a foot.

Both Dick Sanderson and Bert Parks had heard that the Rector was looking for old, seasoned oak to do various repair jobs at St Martins Church. Bert moved like greased lightning. He intimated via a third party that he would take it for the price quoted. An extra sum was agreed for it to be delivered to the *Five Bells*. A total of about 100 cubic feet of old, seasoned oak was delivered and stacked on the back lawn of the pub, for a total sum (including delivery), of £230.

Bert was rubbing his hands with delight. He had already told the Rector that at great personal expense, he had managed to obtain the timber needed for the church repairs, and that he would be willing to pass this on at cost, which was £400. The Rector was duly impressed, but said that he would want the wood supplied in various sawn lengths. Bert readily agreed, money changed hands, and the deal was done. Bert Parks, however, smelled a rat when he saw Captain Dick Sanderson walking about the village smiling happily. He did vaguely wonder why it was that the Captain had not sold the timber directly to the Rector. His smile was an indication that things were not right, but the deal was done. Bert was rubbing his hands, he was going to make a mint!

It was two weeks later, that, with help, Bert managed to get the first timber up on a sawing-horse on the back lawn of the *Five Bells*. Two hours later he was still trying to saw it.

I could have told Bert Parks that I had, many years before, when fixing up the Christmas decorations, tried to push a drawing-pin into the main beam that spanned the house. It was completely impossible. I had tried to knock a nail in to achieve the same end. All I did was bend the nail. In desperation I tried to drill a hole to get a screw in. All that happened was that the drill rotated and went nowhere. It was so impregnated with tar that it was impossible to penetrate. Bert attacked it from time to time. He even paid others to have a go – in the end he gave up. Now he knew why Dick Sanderson still walked about with a smile on his face. He was £230 better off than he had been, and Bert had a pile of timber on his back lawn that he would never get rid of. To the best of my knowledge, fifty years later, some of that timber is still there!

Both Bert Parks and Captain Dick Sanderson, in their respective heydays, were extremely successful in life. Bert ran probably the busiest public house in the area. On summers days it was difficult to get into the bars, and virtually impossible to find a seat on the lawn at the back. Even with this degree of success, Bert still had an eye for business. He would take in shoe repairs for a brother with a club-foot who was a cobbler. He kept him gainfully employed for many years. The *Five Bells* was the meeting place for the *Rat and Tail Club*, the Chelsfield Cricket and Football clubs, and had a darts team that won everything in sight.

Sadly, Bert had a lonely retirement. I suppose that like most landlords he suffered customers because he had to. His idea of retirement was not to mix with the people who had bored him to death during his working life. He gradually took a back seat, only appearing on high days and holidays. He eventually handed over to his son, Doug Parks.

Bert lived in retirement at the house built on the foundations of old Mr Uhlrich's property. As far as I know, apart from his wife and immediate family, Bert Parks enjoyed a lone retirement. Perhaps that was the way he wanted it.

Captain Dick Sanderson had a much more chequered career. A great part of his success came about because of an affinity that he had with his local bank manager. He obtained credit at very favourable terms.

This enabled him to build up an expanding business at a time when anything to do with the building trade was at a premium. He was on the crest of a wave. Apart from a riding stables, his interests consisted of a thriving business with 25 employees, and a fine period property called *Crosshall* in the heart of Chelsfield village.

Sadly for Dick, everything happened at once. He reached retirement, the bottom dropped out of the building trade, and his friendly bank manager moved on to pastures new. The new manager, not as affable as the old one, called in his outstanding debts. In 1966 he closed down the business.

Dick Sanderson, with a lot less fire than before, opened an off-licence at Grays in Essex. This was not a success. After a life of giving orders, he found it difficult to accept the humility of dealing with the more tiresome members of the public. He ended his days living a lonely life in Ramsgate. He died of cancer, in hospital at Margate in 1979.

I have included the story of Bert Parks and Dick Sanderson, because they were part of village life at Chelsfield in the period covered by this book. Life was made richer because of them. They were characters of a place and time and should never be forgotten.

There was another personality who made his mark on the village. This was done in a variety of ways not always known by the local people. He was a man with much genuine goodness – another whose kind will never be seen again. Along with its Lord Mayor of London, Brass Crosby, Chelsfield also had its own Knight of the Realm. Sir Knox-Cunningham lived in *Woodland Cottage* in Chelsfield Lane.

CHAPTER TWENTY-FOUR

Sir Samuel Knox-Cunningham

Sir Samuel Knox-Cunningham was born in Ireland. He came to live in Chelsfield in the early 1940s. Academically, he had been a scholar at Fettes College in Edinburgh, where he was listed as having been a member of the Board of Governors. Educated at Clare College, Cambridge, he attained sporting honours by achieving a heavyweight blue in boxing. He sported two cauliflower ears which testified to this fact. He later became Captain of the University boxing team. He was to become a fully-qualified Amateur Boxing Association judge.

In 1940, Samuel Knox-Cunningham took a commission in the Scots Guards. Shortly after this he was severely injured in an accident involving a motor-cycle which resulted in him being invalided out of the forces and terminated his boxing career.

Samuel Knox-Cunningham advanced in the legal profession, he took the cloth, had chambers in the Law Courts, and became a lawyer and Queen's Council. His particular forté in the legal profession was in the application of law in matters involving marine insurance. He entered politics and became a Member of Parliament for South Antrim. He had the largest Conservative majority in Parliament. In latter years he became personal private secretary to Harold Macmillan. It was this that resulted in his knighthood. He also loved cats!

Lady Knox-Cunningham was President of the All England Womens' Institute. She was a kind and perfect companion to Sir Samuel. Together they quietly pursued a life of untold philanthropy. She too, loved cats!

It is only in later years, that their kindness and generosity to all around them has become known. Apart from assisting financially in the affairs of Chelsfield Cricket Club, Samuel Knox-Cunningham was a great benefactor to the Well Hill Boys' Club.

Boys are notorious for inventing nick-names. Although it must sound dreadful, he was known as 'Obnoxious' Cunningham to all the local boys. This, however, was purely a childlike variation of the 'Knox' part of his name. He was regarded with great affection by all the lads and their parents who he became associated with.

Apart from the financial assistance he gave to deserving causes, Samuel Knox-Cunningham also became a benefactor to those whom he considered deserved a better chance in life who were less fortunate than himself. Bryan Yates and Bob Hogben both benefitted from Sir Samuel's benevolence.

In Bryan's case, having lost his father at an early age, his mother – in order to make ends meet – had to earn an honest crust by doing housework for other people. For years she laboured in fair weather and foul, going up to the landed gentry that lived at the top of Well Hill, doing their chores.

It was obvious that Bryan had great potential in the game of cricket. As a fast bowler he was notorious. In the book by A. G. McDonnel entitled *England Their*

England, the author describes the action of the village fast bowler:

> *The pitch had a hump in the middle; when the bowler (who was the village blacksmith) began his run, he could not be seen by the batsman. The first indication of trouble would be when the ground began to shake. Starlings would rise by the score from the far bound - ary. The bowler would appear, red-faced, going like a steam engine, intent on personally killing the bats - man.*

That was a word-perfect description of Bryan in action! It was agreed generally, by all associated with the game, that when it came to fast bowling, Bryan was certainly of County standard.

Samuel Knox-Cunningham recognised this. Because of his affinity with sport and a recognition of latent talent, he paid for Bryan to be educated at a private school.

Similarly with Bob Hogben. Bob had great potential in the field of boxing. Samuel Knox-Cunningham fostered things along. Regular boxing sessions were held at the Well Hill Boys' Club.

Rather like Grandad Packham's inventions, Sir Samuel's philanthropy had a few built-in design faults. His intentions were all remarkably good, but not always in the best interests of those concerned.

With Bob it was a case of pushing him along, and a bout organised by Sir Knox-Cunningham at Orpington village hall. Bob did not know it, but his opponent was of a semi-professional standard. It was Bob Hogben's first fight. Sadly he had a handicap when it came to the noble art of pugilism. He had a fierce temper that exploded when the blue touch-paper was lighted.

Bob lost his temper within the first few seconds when

he received a smack in the clock that made his ears ring. In a red-hot fury Bob swung wildly in his opponents direction, to receive another smack in the clock that sent him to the canvas. It was all over in minutes. A jumbled Bob, all aspirations of a world championship now gone, went home dejected. Bob's lesson was a hard one, but it was a lesson learned. A while later he fought the same opponent. Bob had learned to control his temper and things were different – it was crash, bang, wallop, and a humbled adversary was left sitting on the floor!

With both Bryan and Bob, Sir Knox-Cunningham would try to educate them to the finer things in life. Once again, a trifle misguided, he would book seats at a London theatre. He and Lady Knox-Cunningham would take a reluctant Bryan and Bob to see *The Taming of the Shrew*, little knowing that they were bored stiff. They would both rather have been at the *Commodore* cinema in Orpington, eating bags of crisps and seeing the latest western adventure.

The Knox-Cunninghams persisted. Bob was even taken to Stratford to see Sheakespeare. Opera, in the shape of Elizabeth Shuman, was also inflicted. He began to dread these occasions, these were fine if your tastes were high-brow. Life at Chelsfield was not like that. We were happier with fish and chips and Bing Crosby. Finally, a few strings were pulled. Bob was enrolled, with Sir Knox-Cunningham's help, at the Kent Farm Institute at Sittingbourne. He graduated with a diploma.

Ultimately, Sir Knox-Cunningham's investment in the two village lads paid off. Bryan became a Quantity Surveyor, and Financial Director to a group of companies. Bob, at first became a farm manager, then the owner of three retail outlets. He is now the owner of a business that supplies accessories to collectors of antique cards.

He is an acknowledged expert in this field. This carries with it consultations by insurance companies in cases of valuation.

Jimmy Watson was another of Sir Knox-Cunningham's proteges. He was the very efficient farm manager of the dairy farm at Bucks Cross. He also had two very attractive daughters, Ella and Nancy, who were the bane of his life. They were hotly pursued by all the young bloods in the area.

Samuel Knox-Cunningham had great plans for Jimmy Watson. Before too long he, unwittingly, was involved in various farming committees. He found, that without knowing it, he was swept up in the affairs of the local Conservative Party. It was obvious that Samuel Knox-Cunningham was doing the pushing.

Whilst it was admirable that he was being urged on to better things, Jimmy Watson, like Bob Hogben (who was made to run before he could walk and was smacked in the clock as a consequence) was pushed on to various local committees. He very soon found himself being put up for election as a Conservative Councillor for the Chelsfield Ward.

It was now, that like Grandad, one of Sir Knox-Cunningham design faults became apparent. Jimmy Watson had the broadest Scottish brogue that it was possible to have. So broad was it, that it was almost impossible to understand. Of all the things in the world that Jimmy Watson could have been, a public speaker was certainly not one of them. Bob Hogben said that when he spoke on Farming Committees, everyone sat silent while Jimmy 'Och'd' and 'Aye'd', throwing in the occasional 'Och they do, they do,' for good measure. 'Hoots mon!' would be followed by 'Ach! Dinna ken the noo, the noo!' There would be thunderous applause as everyone tried to get him to sit down, so that they could get to the beer-tent for some light refreshment. It was the same on the hustings at Conservative Party meetings. People stood fast asleep with their eyes open, as Jimmy's broad vernacular grated away in an indistinguishable language that no one understood.

Sir Knox-Cunningham would proudly smile at the fluency of his protege (having been educated in Scotland, he probably understood all that was being said). It was a pity that no one else did. The odd thing was, that Jimmy Watson was elected. Bryan said that they probably voted for him, to get it all over with and get home to their own firesides.

The time was the early sixties, a cold wind of change was blowing through the village. The dairy farm at Bucks Cross was sold. No more were the black and white Ayrshire cows to be seen wandering leisurely along Hawstead Lane, to turn down a bridle path known as Derly Lane, that led to the lush, green pastures that lay beyond the squires house at Woodlands. Jimmy Watson, now without a job, obtained a position on a farm owned by Christopher Soames in the vicinity of Westerham. This did not last long. He evidently had some affinity for the old place and obtained a position on the nearby farm of Lady Joan Philips at Lullingstone.

Jimmy Watson's daughters, Nancy, and Ella, who everyone fell in love with at one time or another, were both married. Like the rest of us, they left Chelsfield to start lives elsewhere. None of the family were heard of again.

Bob Hogben had obtained a position as a farm manager. He went to live on a farm on the outskirts of Tonbridge.

Bryan went to live at Woodmansterne, in Surrey. He

obtained a position with a construction company with offices in London.

Things had now changed drastically for the Knox-Cunninghams. All their flock had flown. The lads that they had taken such an interest in, from the Well Hill Boys' Club and the Chelsfield Cricket Club, had all grown up and flown. Shops in the village were closing. The quiet lane where they lived now became the entrance to a housing estate. The straw that broke the camels back, was that with the increased traffic on the quiet country lane that passed their cottage, several of their cats were killed. They were cat lovers. They moved to Minchinhampton, in Gloucester. A lone advert in the *Daily Telegraph* announced their passing. They were not heard of again.

CHAPTER TWENTY-FIVE

A Doze by the Fire

On a winters' afternoon, when it was cold and wet, with nothing much to do outside, Grannie and Grandad – accompanied by Grandad's brother, Ern – would get themselves comfortable by the fire. After a while, being knocked out by one of Grannie's monster meat puddings, they would settle down to have forty-winks.

On the occasion that I have in mind, Grannie was bedded-down on the settee in the living-room; she was well tucked-in with a red eiderdown that she kept specifically for that purpose. Only her nose was visible. She contentedly snored her way into well-deserved oblivion.

Ern, who had contentiously taken over Grannie's chair by the fire, had sagged, with sheer weight of pudding, into a similar state of stupor. His head had fallen back, causing his mouth to drop open. This not only exposed his solitary peg-tooth, but caused the most enormous snores to reverberate around the living room. He being stone deaf, slept on!

Grandad; with several glasses of mild and bitter added to his 5 lbs of pudding, was even more unconscious than the the other two. His cap had fallen over one ear. With every exhalation of breath, his lips flapped together making the noise of a two-stroke motorcycle. He seemed to change gear from time to time. The cats, not used to all three going at once, were all crouched under the bureau, backs well up and eyes like saucers, ready to flee at this thunderous racket but unable to get out.

The year was 1950. The war had been over for five years. Prior to his unconscious state, Grandad had been holding forth from behind his newspaper, on how cowardly the Germans had been during the war. "Give the buggers a yard of cold steel," he said, "an' they'll run a bloody mile!" He continued, "I heard tell, that one Tommy wiv a Lee Enfield, held up a complete bloody regiment of ol' Kaiser Bill's Uhlans on 'orseback! All that bloody goose-stepping about, Christ, I'd like ter 'ave 'ad a bloody go at 'em! I'd a showed 'em a thing or two!"

Grannie, with a nap by the fire in mind, had lugged a bucket of coal along from the shed. She piled the fire well up, so that it would last for a few hours and she could rest contented.

Yewtree House, in its time, had been a regular munitions dump. Apart from Grandad's ammunition store of 12 bore cartridges, there were countless boxes of ·22 cartridges, odd ·38 and ·45 calibre bullets were scattered in all manner of places. Grandad threatened that he would take his belt to us if we got anywhere near them. "They're damn deadly," he said. "I knows where they all is. If yer touches 'em, they'll blow yer bloody 'ands orf!" We took his word for it.

Bryan and I contributed, in part, to Grandad's arsenal; luckily he did not know it! Unknown to the three sleeping innocents, three years earlier we had hidden a clip of five ·303 cartridges behind a rusty tin of nails, on a beam in the long shed. We had forgotten that they were there. This was the shed that Grandad kept the fruit-picking ladders in. Our dog, Jip, slept in the same shed. Grannie kept the coal at the other end.

The continual hammering by Grandad in the shed, repairing fruit boxes, chopping the mornings wood, making nesting boxes for Tom-tits; combined with Grannie's Herculean efforts with the coal hammer, all created a set of circumstances that led to an explosive situation.

The hammering had shaken the ·303 cartridges from their place on the shelf into the coal, and Grannie shot them in the fire!

In being over-enthusiastic with the coal-hammer, Grannie had dislodged the clip of bullets, which had neatly fallen in the coal bucket!

Grannie vehemently insisted afterwards that "there weren't no bullits in the coal when I shot it on!"

A humiliated Grandad said, "You wouldn't know a bloody bullet if you woz a damn-well sittin' on it!"

It must have been at least an hour later; they were all in top gear shaking the rafters.

Grandad was dreaming that he had been at the battle of the Somme. He had taken a trench of German troops single-handed. He was at at the point of receiving the Victoria Cross from the King at Buckingham Palace.

Grannie, in a similar situation, was trying to heat one of the new tinned Christmas puddings, in a saucepan of water on the fire.

Ernie's mind was a blank. It always was, he never even spoke of having a dream.

It must have been an hour later that it happened. With a thunderous crash the fire exploded. The first bullet knocked a complete piece out of the kitchen table leg. Grandad shot bolt upright, cap falling off, and exclaimed, "No, Sir. I did it wiv an 'and grenade!"

Grannie looked over the top of the eiderdown and said, "That weren't no 'and grenade, I must 'ave let the water get low!"

Another incredible explosion, blew what was left of the fire all over the hearth. This time the bullet hit the chest of drawers on the opposite side of the room under which the cats were crouching. They came out in all directions. They hurled themselves at the closed windows, knocking all Grannie's ornaments over in the process. Condensed milk began running out of a hole in the bottom drawer of the chest of drawers (that had not been there before). Pandemonium ensued.

Grandad, the hero of the Somme, shouted "Bugger the wimmin and children, I'm orf!" he flew in the direction of the pantry.

Another 'BANG!' helped him on his way. This time hitting a bunch of peacock feathers in a vase that Grannie kept, because it was said that they brought good luck!

Grannie, now sitting upright, said "It 'ent right they should be a'sellin' puddin's that goes orf like that. They 'ent done me fire no good."

Grandad, looking out through a crack in the pantry door, shouted, "They 'ent done me bloody trousers no good either! 'Ave they gorn yet?"

"Who?" said Grannie.

"Them bloody Germins!" said Grandad.

The cats had now joined Grandad in the pantry. "Git out from under me bloody feet then!" he shouted as he trod on one of them. There was a sound of saucepans falling on the floor. "Git out the bloody way then!" he yelled.

"There 'ent no Germins," said Grannie, "only puddin's!"

"Puddin's don't make 'oles in bloody walls!" said Grandad, adding, "Some of yer buggers does!"

By this time they were both wide awake. Grannie did some detective work. "I didn't 'ave no puddin's on!" she said. "I must 'ave bin dreamin'." Grandad, coming out of the pantry, said, "'ee was jest a'givin' me the bloody Victoria Cross, too!"

"Wot's that fer then?" said Grannie.

"Bravery!" said Grandad.

"Didn't look none too brave ter me," said Grannie. "Wot does they gives yer for bein' frightened then?"

Grandad looked narked. "I 'ent frightened of no one!" he said. "I'd take on the 'ole bleedin' Germin army!"

"Didn't look like it ter me," said Grannie. "You went through the pantry door as if yer damn trousers woz on fire!"

"They bloody-well woz!" said an irate Grandad, helping one of the cats out of the pantry with a well-aimed foot. He was mortally offended that his courage should have been doubted.

He furiously patted the rear of his trousers as if putting a fire out. "Anyway," he said, beginning to poke around what was left of the fire. "This 'ere's the cause of the trouble!"

Shining brightly amongst the pile of coal left at the back of the fire, were the two remaining brass cartridges left from the clip of five.

"Is they bullits?" asked Grannie. "'spects the Germins left 'em there!"

"Stand clear!" said Grandad, knowing that they had not been near the heat and were quite safe. "These buggers could blow yer arse orf!"

Taking the shovel, he gently lifted them from the pile of coal, and on tip-toe, cautiously went out to the waterbutt and dropped them in.

"How's that fer the action of a frightened man," he said cockily. "There 'ent many men as would do that with an unexploded bomb!"

Grannie made him sit down and take a shot of whisky, purely for medicinal purposes she said. It was to treat him for the shock, which she said he must have suffered from that extreme act of bravery. Grandad was happy, he had once more established himself as a hero in Grannie's eyes. She was his true love and the only one that mattered in his life. It was important to him that he be held in her highest esteem.

With Grannie it was different. Of course she appreciated his noble act. Of course he was her only true love. The simple truth, however, was that by dosing him with a double shot of whisky, and pandering to his inflated ego, she made him forget that it was she who had chucked a load of ·303 bullets on the fire, and had nearly blown them all to kingdom come.

Grannie cleaned up the mess while Grandad finished up the whisky. She once again lit the fire. Before too long the old kettle, black with soot, was singing a merry tune. A grey winters afternoon was soon made brighter by the sound of spoons in tea-cups. Piles of burnt toast were made with Grannie's bent toasting fork and covered with thick country butter.

It was at this time that the cats began to return, still with eyes as wide as saucers and treading warily. It was also at this time that Uncle Ern blinked, and came back to the land of the living. He looked vaguely disgruntled.

"Wot's up wiv you then?" enquired Grandad.

"Don't like the bleedin' winter.' he said.

"Ent nuthin' wrong wiv it," said Grandad.

"Nuthin' ever 'appens," said Ernie.

"That's wot you bloody-well think!" said Grandad.

Ernie drank his tea. He nodded off again, unaware of what had happened.

"What 'ee don't know 'ee don't 'ave ter worry about!" said Grandad happily.

CHAPTER TWENTY-SIX

The Winds of Change

It is odd how the world turns a full circle; it hits you back when you are least expecting it. That's what happened to the buses. I suppose that some would say it was the march of progress and things are better because of it. I do not. I liked a bus service that ran on time, where the buses were always clean, where the conductor who you knew by his first name always had a helping hand and a cheery smile; where courtesy was the rule rather than the exception.

It was actually possible to catch a 477 bus from Chelsfield village, that went to Orpington, St Mary Cray, and to Swanley, Wilmington, Hextable and Dartford.

Our own bus was the 431 and the 431a. In 1935 this was a chubby little bus operated by a driver only. It then progressed to a double-decker with a full crew. This was superseded by a very long single-decker with both driver and conductor; this posed a problem – it had a long wheel-base and could not negotiate the corners. Finally the latest double-decker took over. It ran for more years than I care to remember.

The 431a ran from Sevenoaks, via a multitude of villages, to Kelvin Parade near to Crofton. The 431 covered the same route, but terminated at Orpington station. There was also a country bus known as the 402. This ran from Sevenoaks, via Dunton Green, Knockholt, Pratts Bottom, Green-St-Green, Farnborough, Locks Bottom, to Bromley North station.

Pride of place went to an express service called the Green-Line. This plied between Tonbridge and Windsor via Victoria. It was the Blue-Riband of London Transport. It was faster, with fewer stops, than normal services.

All London Transport country buses were sympathetically-coloured, dark green. This blended in with the lush countryside. All London Transport town buses were bright red. At least they were not covered with gaudy posters. They looked like buses; you could see them coming from a mile away.

Orpington had its fair share of red buses. Apart from the 51, which ran from Farnborough to Sidcup, via Green-St-Green, Orpington, and St Mary Cray, there was the 61 service that plied between Bromley Garage and Chislehurst, via Locks Bottom, Orpington and Petts Wood.

It will be seen that both Chelsfield and Orpington were well-served by the country and town services of the London Transport Bus Company.

This dependence on local bus services was a sign of the times. It must be remembered that very few people were wealthy enough to own a motor car. Bicycles were the main means of transport that people aspired to.

Although it was the advent of the internal combustion engine – in the form of the bus – that opened the field of choice, both social and in commerce, to the people of the area, it also brought about the decline of Chelsfield village and a way of life. It was the further development of this invention – in the form of the motor car, that provided convenient transport for all, and ultimately assured the demise of the bus service.

It does not seem all that long ago, that as a child, I rode on the last open-topped bus with my mother, as far as the *Five Bells* in Chelsfield. We paused for a while, for a glass of Tizer and Smiths Crisps (with the blue twist of salt), before walking over the fields to see Grannie and Grandad. I was bitten by a monkey that Bert Parks kept on the lawn behind the pub. I bawled all the way across the fields to the old cottage.

It is probably part of the human psyche, that only good memories are remembered with affection. However, it would be incorrect to assume that the buses operated by London Transport were all sweetness and light. Not all bus crews were the kindly souls that I have portrayed.

There were the vindictive conductors who, at Orpington railway station, would take a vicious delight in ringing the bell for their driver to depart, as the main line train from London was arriving at the platform. The arrival time of the train was the same as the departure time of the bus. Both the driver and his conductor would be in hysterics at the sight of twenty portly gentlemen, running flat out, in a confusion of bowler hats, briefcases, and rolled umbrellas, trying to catch the bus as it accelerated away down the station approach. Many times I have been in this position, hoping, as I sprinted after the bus, that there would be a queue at the bus stop at the Maxwell Hotel, to delay the bus and save me from an hours wait for the next one.

There was also great irritation, when the bus arrived at the bus stop at Orpington War Memorial, to find it was jammed with the same portly gentlemen, and was too full for you to get on. They all got out half a mile up the road, leaving you to either get the 477 bus as far as the village; and to walk the mile home across the fields in the mud, or to wait another hour for the next bus to arrive. It all depended on whether there was an amicable conductor on board. If there was, he would pack you all in (despite the complaints of the city gentlemen) knowing that the bus would empty out within the next few minutes. If not, only five standing would be allowed. Your fate would be an hour in the teeming rain. You would pray for the time when you could have your own motor car.

I have written previously, of our very odd habit of changing names for no apparent reason. The Local Defence Volunteers (LDV) became The Home Guard, the Air Raid Precautions (ARP) became the Civil Defence. In latter years it still goes on. The atomic power station at Sellafield became Windscale. It is now Cumbernaud. The General Post Office, which once handled the telephone system, seems to be known as either British Telecommunications, British Telecom, or just plain 'BT'. Try to find a particular department of The National Health Service (NHS). This has become The Department of Health and Social Security (DHSS) and the Department of Social Security (DSS). The DHSS will not answer an enquiry that should go to the DSS and vice versa. There seems to be a Department of Health (DOH) as well. The world seems to have gone quite mad.

I mention this peculiarity, to explain an anomaly that must confuse my reader. It is the confusion of names concerning the highways and byways of the area in which I once lived.

Once upon a time, there was a beautiful bridle path that ran off to the right at the top of Well Hill. It was known as Well Hill Lane. It formed part of a walk that we would take on Sunday afternoons that led to Shoreham Woods. It eventually became a picturesque avenue of pine trees and emerged near to the game-keepers cottage in Shoreham Lane. It was here that Tommy Blundell settled in the mid 1750s and began the Chelsfield line of the Blundell family. This bridle path is now known by the imaginative name of Reservoir Road.

Well Hill itself, for some obscure reason, is now Rock Hill. The new Well Hill, is a very minor section of lane that turns left, near to the top of the present Rock Hill, at the place where Alwens shop once stood.

To confuse matters even more, the track that runs off to the left at the bottom of Rock Hill, that we once knew as Back Hill, is now known as Pump Hill Lane. This ancient lane was once a principle route that was alleged to have existed before Well Hill. It had at its beginning, the only fresh-water spring in the area. It was used by the local populace for their supply of drinking water. In later years the spring was capped and a tap installed. It now seems to have been removed. The constant dampness of the lane at this point, however, would indicate that although officialdom might decide to remove a water supply, nature seems to know right from wrong, and will have its own way in the end.

Back Hill, led to what was allegedly a haberdashers that sold ale as a sideline. The haberdashery side closed in time – what was left became the *Kent Hounds* public house. It was at the farthest extremity of our parish and was only visited for a glass of cider on the odd summers' evening. It was a remote place, it's main claim to fame being that three council boundaries met there. It was said that one of its public rooms was in the Sevenoaks area (the landlord paid rates for that room to the Sevenoaks council), the other parts of the property were in the Orpington and Swanley areas.

At the bottom of Rock Hill, the left fork is now known as Jubilee Road. This is a recent innovation, it was always known as Maypole Road. It leads to the area that was known to all as Maypole. Bus timetables referred to its junction with Shoreham Lane (now known as Maypole Road) as 'Maypole Corner'. At a stroke, the hamlet of Maypole (a derivation of the old name 'Maple') was removed from the face of the earth. I should add for clarification, that Shoreham Lane once ran from Bucks Cross to an odd hamlet named Timberden Bottom and then on to Shoreham village.

Timberden Bottom was the site of a working hermitage. In my time a few monks were still in residence. Standing in the gardens were tiny wooden cells that resembled chicken houses. Each had a cross on its roof. The monks could be seen in rough sandals and heavy-hooded habits with large gold crosses embroidered on the backs, labouring in the gardens. They would care for the vagrants who walked to them from the workhouse at Farnborough. They were allowed to stay for three days, and were then sent packing to walk the five miles back again.

Between the bottom or Rock Hill and Jubilee Corner, there is a turning to the left that leads past a row of council houses that were known as 'Kilnfields'. We always considered that we were socially superior to the inhabitants of these properties. On reflection, at least, they had internal bathrooms and toilets that flushed, which was more than we had. The truth of the matter was that they were infinitely better equipped than we were. The lane that ran past the council houses was known by the same name and went as far as the crossroads at the *Bo-Peep*. The name "Kilnfields' does not appear to exist any more. This road has been named Hollybush Lane.

There is a bridle path that runs from the council houses to the old Shoreham Lane (Maypole Road). This formed the southern boundary of our property. It fronted the black cottages once owned by Mr Bowen for the use of his workers at the timber yard. Where it joins the old Shoreham Lane, there is an area known as Greenels Eyn. This was a favourite place of Grannie's, where evening primroses once grew, she would always pause here and say "Them's evenin' primroses allus growed 'ere." This bridle path was extensively used by all the delivery vehicles in the area. Mr and Mrs Fox would use it for their pony and trap, all the people from the council houses would sprint along it when they heard the bus pulling away from the *Bo-Peep*, going flat out to reach the bus stop at Jubilee Corner (Maypole Corner) before the bus did. This bridle path was the *real* Hollybush Lane. This too seems to have gone forever. The track that is left is barely passable. The end at the black cottages seems to be jammed with a conglomeration of motor cars. The only association that it seems to have with the past, is that Mr Fox's old house – although a shadow of its former self – is still called *Hollycroft*.

The road to Chelsfield village, to the right at the bottom of Rock Hill (Well Hill), is still Hawstead Lane. The only apparent change is in the derelict condition of its hedges and the appearance of an old-car dump close to Squire Waring's house at *Woodlands* (now Cannock House School). Mr Waring's and Mr Tomlin's chauffeur, Arthur Mitchell, lived with his wife and son Reggie, in a small bungalow next to the big house at *Woodlands*. It is now unrecognisable – under its blanket of moss and mildew – as a place of habitation. They would be shocked at its present appearance.

Why the Packham family left Eynsford at the turn of

the century and settled in Chelsfield, no one knows, but it was at the Squires house that Grandad Packham began his working life as head butler. At least that's what he told Grannie. This is a matter of some doubt. I suspect that Grandad, in order to impress Grannie, exaggerated his position somewhat. One becomes a head butler after many years of service. As Grandad was still a young man when he courted and married Grannie, his position at that grand establishment was probably that of a simple man-servant.

A fine row of majestic beech trees once stood opposite to the Squires house in Hawstead Lane. These were truly magnificent – they were part of the beauty of Chelsfield village. For no reason that I know of, in a sheer act of vandalism, they were simply torn down. Sadly, all that remains, apart from nostalgic memories of their beauty, are the recollections of delicate shades of spring green, and the soft russet tones of autumn, with which they graced the memories of my youth. One wonders at the damage that can be done by an individual with an axe and a chain-saw, who passes our way in an instant of time, and despoils forever, a heritage that is not his to destroy.

Between the Squires house at *Woodlands* and Bucks Cross, there is a field to the left that runs across to Albert Blott's house. It is the field that is opposite to Mount Hall. This was the place in which five Ayrshire cows were killed by an oil bomb during the last war. It also contained seven magnificent walnut trees that were as permanent as the rock of Gibraltar. The only thing left is a gnarled, dead, remnant of one of them.

At this point in Hawstead Lane, to the right, there is all that remains of a landway known as Derly Lane. It is still there, but only a shadow of its former self. Access is

*Plate 35: The Wesleyan Chapel built 1872 in Chelsfield. Now the home of
old Doug Parks, son of old Bert Parks*

Plate 36: Chelsfield Church, St Martin of Tours, where all the people of my time are now sleeping peacefully

Plate 37: Well Hill Church. Where Mrs Jefferys played the organ, and Mr Jefferys regularly shouted at the lay reader

Plate 38: Bert Parks, the landlord of the Five Bells, *and unelected Mayor of Chelsfield*

Plate 39: Captain Dick Sanderson. The bain of Bert Parks, who insisted on drinking in the public bar of the Five Bells

Plate 40: Captain Sanderson with his twenty-five employees, at 'Crosshall' in the village of Chelsfield

Plate 41: The philanthropist, Sir Samuel, and Lady Knox-Cunningham

Plate 42: Mr Bernard 'Bunny' Bowen of the timber-yard family, ready to stop Hitler

Plate 43: Syd Stevens, on leave after the battle for Casino in Italy

Plate 44: Joan Blundell, Bryan, Little Nell, at the Blue Lagoon *swimming pool at St Mary Cray*

Plate 45: Complete group photograph of the Bo-Beep *outing of 1952*

Plate 46: The Maypole Boys in a tug-of-war contest at the village fête.
Jack (John) Divine in shirt sleeves at cente of picture

Plate 47: A 'Sack' fight: Bryan Yates and Eric Costin at the village fête

Plate 48: The last meeting of old friends: Chelsfield Village Hall, 1994

Plate 49: The old garden path, from the gate at the top of the garden

One day we'll sail the depths of space, and waken in another place,
There we'll quietly stand and wait, for each other at the garden gate.
Hand in hand we'll wander through, the old back door, to dear ones who,
have waited long, for us at last, to join them from the old times past.
Dorrie, Bryan, you and me, with Gran and Grandad making tea.
"Where 'ave yer bin?" Gran will say, "We thought you'd gorn an' lost
    yer way,
"It's bin so long, we've missed yer so, the reaper's got no more ter
    mow.
"I know too, that you'd like to learn, we're damn-well stuck wiv brother
    Ern."
And that is how it all will end, no more troubled paths to wend.
All round the fire, feeling fine, together till the end of time.

*Plate 50: The last birthday message to my mother in 1992. The year that she
floated over the clouds and far away*

closed to all but pedestrians. I suppose that the iron posts that block its entrance are a sign of the times. They are there to prevent the dumping of rubbish, with which the countryside now seems to be contaminated.

A few years ago, part of Chelsfield life, would have been the cows. After milking, wandering unattended, stopping from time to time to munch the lush pasture at the sides of the landway, back to their fields at the end of Derly Lane. We would explore its green pastures looking for mushrooms. We have been chased by the odd bull or two. Bryan and I saw a cow giving birth. Bryan cried when he saw a cowman holding the cow's tail up. He was sure that he was holding an axe and was about to kill the poor creature. We held an inquest when we arrived back at the old cottage. We wanted to know what had been going on. Grandad, put on the spot, nipped into the shed and banged about on a shoe-last as if his life depended on it. Grannie tipped a frying-pan full of the mushrooms that we had gathered (she was cooking them with huge rashers of bacon) straight into the fire. We were decidedly upset, we had been up since five o'clock that morning gathering them. We could not understand what all the fuss was about.

Bucks Cross farm (without the cows) now seems derelict. One rarely sees any life there. The buildings are in a state of decay. Odd farm implements stand rusting. The farm house seems empty now; without the laughter of Nancy and Ella Watson, and no Jim Watson being urged on by Sir Knox Cunningham, it is now only an empty shell. A place of ghosts.

The situation is the same with Hewitts Farm. Dereliction has enveloped a place that was once a hive of activity. Farm workers have gone that once worked the fields by hand. Cattle are silent that filled the vast cow-sheds of this once great farm. Decay is apparent by rusting machinery, broken fences, collapsing rooves, and broken walls. The ghosts of Old Stanley May of Broke Farm, and his son, Henry May from Hewitts Farm, are now tilling the fields in pastures new. One hopes they are not aware of the fate that has overtaken the great estates they left behind.

One road that did not have a name to change, is the one that runs north from the junction in the centre of the village. Its route takes it between the old chapel and the school. It bears left after a hundred yards at a house known as *Rounds*. It is here that Chelsfield Lane begins its course to Georges pig farm and St Mary Cray. It is also where a direct hit by a V1 Flying Bomb destroyed Lillys Farm in the last war.

As this road was once the main London to Hastings road, this section was probably known as Orpington Road, Chelsfield. The properties on its route within the village would not have needed an address. *Rounds*, the school, the chapel, and the rectory. It passes a pond, this holds dismal memories of duckings on cold afternoons after Sunday School, to squelch home, wet and miserable in soggy misery; it ended at Court Road.

In recent times a name board has appeared in the village which states that its name is now Warren Road. This is not true – Warren Road is part of 'new' Chelsfield. It begins on the *other* side of Court Road. It is a sign that the old village is being taken over by the usurpers from the other side!

CHAPTER TWENTY-SEVEN

The Sands of Time

It is difficult, when writing of a particular time, to please everyone. People see things from their own point of view in a brief moment of time; they forget that things change, nothing stays the same. One has only to note the fate of the big houses and the people in them.

When the church ran low in funds, *The Rectory* – once the grandest house in the village – was bought by Norman Butler, a director of the Bank of England, . *Butlers* was requisitioned by the army in the early part of the war. Nothing was heard of the family again. The derelict mansion was converted to a luxury hotel, finally becoming Chelsfield Park Hospital. The Rector moved into *Court Lodge* which then became the new rectory. Not quite so grand as before, but still a house of some standing. A shrinking church called from more economies. Another move was made to a house near to Lilleys Farm at the top of the village. This then became the rectory; it was large, Victorian in style, not as opulent as *Court Lodge*. The decline continued with the sale of this property. It was demolished and a small development of new houses built on the site. The present rectory was built where the old *Reading Room* once stood at the centre of the village. It is an impressive building, but in the modern style. An example of one of the new buildings that destroyed the character of the old village. It is but a shadow of its predecessors.

So it will be seen, that in the relatively short period of time covered by these chronicles, Chelsfield village has had four different rectory's, each administered respectively by the Reverends Follett-Baugh, Mackay, Woodall, and Virgo.

It was said that the death duties payable on the death of old Stanley May, financially crippled his son Henry May. He sold up, and is said to have moved to somewhere in Hampshire. He has never been heard of again.

Broke Farm, on the opposite side of the valley from Hewitts Farm, became a golf course. The Waring family, finding the upkeep of *Woodlands* prohibitive, sold it and bought Hewitts Farm. Like the Rector, they moved down a grade. A Mr Tomkin took over the squire's house at *Woodlands*. This is now Cannock House School. Nothing more seems to have been heard of the Tompkin family. The Waring's endeavoured to keep the flag of opulence flying by still employing a chauffeur. In my time they had a total of three chauffeurs. Mr Toms, who lived above a stable at Lillys Farm, Arthur Mitchell who lived with his wife and son in a small bungalow next to their property in Hawstead Lane, and Frank Skinner, who lived at Jubilee Corner and worked for them when they moved to Hewitts Farm.

Any record of the great houses of Chelsfield, seems to omit the obvious. There is a property in Chelsfield Parish that, not because it is an architectural masterpiece, but because it is unusual and literally stands, head and shoulders, above all others.

To me, and as far as I know, to all the older inhabitants of Chelsfield and Maypole, it has always stood, like a beacon, indicating the place where our home was. I have seen it from Essex, and from all over Kent. When arriving home in later years from travels abroad, my heart would be lifted at seeing it from the train at Orpington railway station.

I refer of course to the 'house on the hill', the property known to all of us irreverently, as *The Pepper Pot*. This was simply because, from a distance, its silhouette against the skyline looked remarkably like an ornate Victorian pepper pot. Its correct name was *The White House*, the name by which it was known by Mr and Mrs Lambert who lived there in the early 1920s. Mrs Lambert, on the death of her husband, built a small bungalow by the side of the Maypole meadow opposite to *Yewtree House*, the cottage in which we all lived.

Whoever bought the property from Mrs Lambert promptly changed its name to *The Chestnuts*, a rather suburban name for such a striking edifice. There were in fact, chestnut trees to one side of the property, but these were small. They formed part of the general shrubbery and were of no consequence. They eventually grew and monopolised the garden. The replaced poplar trees withered away. The mature chestnut trees were destroyed in the great hurricane of 1987.

This change of name was an enigma to the local people, if anything, the house should have been called *The Poplars*. The two impressive poplar trees after all, stood like sentinels by the side of it. These were as much a landmark as the house itself. The original poplars were known to all as 'Adam' and 'Eve'. We had a piece of bark from one of them on the wall of the old cottage. It was inscribed by Grandad. *Adam and Eve, destroyed by lightning in 1921*. They were replaced and flourished. Today, two gnarled stumps covered with ivy are all that remain. The memory of these two magnificent trees, together with the house, will remain forever as denoting, with Chelsfield Church, the eastern and western boundaries of Well Hill, Maypole, and Chelsfield, they signified the area that was home to all of us.

One or two interesting statistics are relevant concerning this house. It was occupied for many years during the 1970s by three gentlewomen. Their names were Grace Jackson, Phyllis Angel, and Silvia Stewart. They were probably the last of an age that dedicated itself to preserving the property. The gardens were immaculate. They were looked after by Arthur French, the brother of George French. Arthur lived in the cottage next to the *Rock and Fountain* and George lived with his old mother in the small cottage adjacent to the *White House*. A superb tennis court graced its grounds. These soared away towards London, giving an uninterrupted view over Chelsfield and Orpington. It was the nearest thing to flying, without actually being in an aircraft.

An impressive swimming pool completed a picture of an elegant lifestyle that we had only ever dreamed about.

I was informed by Grace Jackson that the house is reputed to be 750 ft above sea level, considerably higher than Biggin Hill aerodrome. It was built in 1896. It is possible from its observatory, to see five counties, Kent, Essex, Middlesex, Surrey and Sussex. St Paul's Cathedral is easily seen although sixteen miles away, and Alec Stevens (one of the Stevens boys) can remember watching the Crystal Palace burning in 1934 from its garden. On a good day one can see as far as Hampstead Heath in North London.

According to Grace Jackson, there were problems with the plumbing. This is understandable when one considers that the house stands well above the local reservoir. It would seem that to get water up to the water tank, an awful chore, was in starting the petrol engine needed to do the job. Grace Jackson informed me that she and her friends swam in the pool in the early 1970s, but found with the passing of time, that the cost of the chemicals needed for purification and the expense of heating the water to protect the pool in the winter, was prohibitive.

After they left, the *Pepper Pot*, like so many other properties at that time, fell into a state of neglect. The tennis court and pool are in a sorry state. The present owners seem to be trying to put things right. Such an elegant house with so many memories deserves to be cared for.

CHAPTER TWENTY-EIGHT

Memories of the Good Times

It is sad that such a happy time should have gone forever. This was brought home to me recently, when talking to a comparative stranger in Chelsfield village. He remarked how much he had enjoyed reading my two previous books. I said that it was incredible that it was such a short time ago. He replied sadly, that these times would never come back. They had gone forever, he said.

When I repeated this later to my friend Bob Hogben, he looked very pensive. "I'd never thought of it like that before," he said thoughtfully, "Brings it home with a bit of a shock, when it's said that way."

I reflected on this later. I thought of all the things that had come and gone in our time, of a way of life that was simple, and without stress. Of the kind people that I have known who really cared. Of world events that would never happen again. Of the technological developments that had surpassed our wildest dreams. It had all happened in *our* time. We had seen a change from the old to the new.

When I see the quiet country lanes of Maypole and Chelsfield, it is inconceivable that so many events could have happened in those peaceful byways of the area in which I lived.

It was the time of the British motor cycle; of the Scott,

Douglas, Calthorp, Sunbeam and Zenith. In latter times it was the Norton, Triumph, AJS, BSA, and Matchless. The magic of a Norton on full bore on the TT circuit, the crackle of a 500 cc BSA Gold Star at 100 mph past Johnsons café, were sounds that made the heart pound. Their like will never be heard again. Whatever happened to Jock West, Harold Daniels, Eric Oliver, Derek Minter and John Surtees? What became of the mighty Vincent HRD and Jeff Duke?

The camaraderie, when you pulled in for a rest at the side of the road, and within minutes other motor cyclists would stop and ask if you wanted any help. Some of them were so keen, that if you were not quick, they would be taking your machine to pieces to see what was wrong.

When a Sunday afternoons entertainment, was sitting in the sun, by the bend on River Hill, watching steaming motor cars with red-faced families, heads covered with knotted handkerchiefs, coming back from the coast. You could pick out the ones that were not going to make it; they would be steaming more than the others. We would leap to their aid, to push them merrily on their way. Everyone had punctures, one a day was the norm, tyre levers and a starting handle were all part of a day out.

Like the motor cycle, it was also a time of the motor car, of the 'bull-nosed' Morris and Austin Seven, of the Riley, Armstrong-Sidley, Jowett, Rover, and Ford Eight (of which you could have any choice of colour providing it was black). There were three-wheeled Morgans with JAP engines (nothing to do with the Japanese, simply J. A. Parker) bolted on their fronts, open valve springs clattering about on their tops. Elegant Rolls Royces, Daimlers, Lanchesters, Humber 'Snipes' and 'Green Label' Bentleys (with mighty leather straps to hold their bonnets down), all completed a picture of opulence with which we were not associated.

It was still possible to buy Cleveland, Regent, and National Benzole petrols. Garages checked your oil and water levels without being asked. Mechanics were not parts-swoppers; they did wonders with copper wire. When cars were part-exchanged, sales staff spread their profits over the resale of your old vehicle, and the price they made on the one they were selling you, not taking you to the cleaners by profiting on both transactions. It was a time of the world land-speed record breakers; Captain George Eyston and the Golden Arrow, John Cobb and the Napier-Railton, Malcolm Campbell and Bluebird. What incredible times they were.

In the field of aviation, its seems impossible to believe that it once took five days to fly to India. The Handley Page HP 47s of Imperial Airways cruised at 150 knots. In a headwind of 100 knots (not uncommon), they actually covered the ground, with a compliment of twelve passengers, at a speed of 50 mph. It would be quite possible in this day and age, to do it quicker by car. These flying machines were deemed to be ships that flew; everything about them was nautical. The ones that landed on water were called flying boats (which I suppose they were). The American flying boats were called Clippers. The gas-bags that flew were called air-ships. The one in charge wore naval dress; he was either the captain or the pilot. Right and left were port and starboard. Speeds were in knots. Control columns had spoked wheels as on sailing ships. It was common for these machines (because of mechanical or navigational problems) to land anywhere suitable. We had one in the fields near Well Hill, another near Court Road, and yet another on the Shoreham side of Timberden Bottom. Four people perished in that incident. There was always a triangular memorial stone, with the names of the poor people inscribed on it to commemorate their passing. It, together with a most incredible life-sized, carved, wooden crucifix, has now gone.

Junkers JU 52 aircraft of the German Luft-Hansa airlines, regularly landed at Croydon airport; they were covered in swastikas and seemed to be made from corrugated iron. The very early ones had the pilot sitting in a fully-exposed cockpit behind the central engine. The passengers all seemed to be big men with shaven heads and 'Kaiser Bill' moustaches; they wore lederhosen and yodelling hats and seemed to spend all their time photographing airfields in southern England.

In the development of flying boats the Germans led the field. They built the Dornier DO X. It was made almost entirely of wood, had a crew of fifteen, and carried over 170 passengers. It had twelve engines arranged in tandem, six pushing and six pulling. It actually flew to America.

The Italians tried to out-do them by building the Caproni CA 60. This had eight engines, nine wings (three at the front, three at the back, and another three in the middle) giving a total wing span over 900 feet. It was said that separate pilots steered both ends. The inevitable happened. In argumentative Italian fashion they turned different ways on take off. It broke in half and landed in two pieces on a beach. It was left there. We did our bit; our contribution was the pick-a-back aircraft named the Maia and Mercury. Its purpose was to get mail to America in one hop. The idea was, that the smaller seaplane took off from the mother craft when it was two-thirds across the Atlantic. It rejoined – when the mail had been delivered – at St Johns in Newfoundland. It was found, however, that it was just as easy to refuel at St Johns and carry on as before, rather than carry another aircraft across the Atlantic. It was a great technological achievement but completely useless. It use was abandoned.

Such was the development of our own fighting aircraft, that the newly introduced Bristol 'Blenheim', a light bomber, turned out to be 50 mph faster than our top fighter of that time. We progressed, however. We won the Schneider Trophy outright. It was not publicised that we were the only entrants.

Air displays were incredible affairs. Formation aerobatics were carried out with aircraft chained together at their wing-tips. It was all very inspiring. So was a German parachutist called Hans Klemm who flew with bat-like wings. His parachute refused to deploy. He hit the main road at Biggin Hill in front of a bus. What was left of him was well and truly finished off by the bus. They had to take the bus driver and half the passengers sitting on the top deck to hospital suffering from shock. They evidently had a grandstand view.

We would have our own grandstand view every Saturday morning. For this was the time of the cinema. We lived for our weekly visit to a dream world of make believe. It would either be the tuppeny rush at the *Palace* (otherwise known as the 'Bug Hutch'), at Orpington Pond, or Flash Gordon and an awful organist on a Wurlitzer organ (which everyone hated) at the *Commodore* by Orpington War Memorial, or the same thing at the *Embassy* at Petts Wood. You queued for an hour to get in, that was all part of the fun, you booed and stamped your feet at the baddies, cheered the goodies. After two hours in the dark, you came squinting into brilliant sunshine. This made your forehead ache, your eyes hurt, and together with a hoarse throat, meant that it had been a good film.

Actors like Wallace Beery, Clark Gable, Adolph Menjou, Don Ameche, were as well known to you as your own neighbours. Actresses like Dorothy Lamour, Rita Hayworth, Joan Fontaine, Doris Day and Jane Russell, competed for your affections with the girl next door; everyone was in love with them at one time or another. The list was endless, Paul Henreid, Jane Wyman, Van Heflin, Alexis Smith, Claud Rains, Maureen O'Hara, and Bette Davis were all part of our lives.

But progress, in the form of television, killed the cinema, and with it the stars that made our dreams. Where did they all go? Whatever happened to the *Commodore* and *Palace* in Orpington, the *Embassy* at Petts Wood, the *Gaumont* at Bromley, the *Flea Pit* and the *Plaza* at Sevenoaks?

It was the same, to a degree, with Saturday night dances. A dance was the only occasion, when you were lawfully allowed to put your arms around a member of the opposite sex without being arrested. It was even possible in a dance known as a 'general excuse-me', to break up a couple in order to dance with the girl of your dreams. But, as in all things, progress takes a hand. New dances became the fashion. It would seem that the thing to do was to stand four feet away from your partner, look the other way, and to jerk your limbs about as if you had lost all control of them. This was all accompanied by pulsating lights, and music so loud as to drown any intelligent conversation.

Dancing after all, was a form of courtship; it was a means of meeting a desirable young lady and establishing a relationship. When fashion meant looking the other way and not getting near your chosen partner. When it was not possible to see them in the dark, or to converse because of the volume of the music, then it was obvious that it was not going to be a winner! Like the cinemas, the dance halls became bingo halls, the whole world seemed to be full of bingo halls. These are now full of chain-smoking old-age pensioners, who want somewhere warm to sit, with a chance of winning a stuffed donkey or a plastic tea set, on cold winter afternoons.

One wonders where all the youngsters have gone that went to these dances. I can remember, near to Bowens timber yard, a slightly refined venue named Heverswood. On a Sunday afternoon, one could dance for two hours, to a three-piece band (piano, saxophone and drums), sit in your own private alcove with four friends, have a pot of tea for five, jam with brown bread and butter, a plate of fancy cakes, strawberries and cream, all for the sum of 60p (in todays money), for five! All fully inclusive.

It was the same with public houses. A public house was once a convivial place, almost a club, where the landlord was a genuine friend, where one sat in clean, genial surroundings, and passed a pleasant hour or two in conversation with friends and acquaintances over a pint of ale. If you fancied lording it, there was always the saloon bar. The drinks would cost you more, but the extra cost was acceptable for the more refined surroundings and a better class of company.

Breweries in all their wisdom, decided to change all that. They sacked the landlords – managers were cheaper. Sadly their interests were purely mercenary. Many of them did not even live on their own premises, they felt no need to befriend the customers. "Knock all the bars into one," they said. "Get the fruit machines in and wake 'em all up with a juke box!" With the clatter of fruit machines and the deafening racket of the juke boxes, the days of the quiet chat were numbered. "Let's get the manual workers in," they said. "Let them all sit with their overalls covered in cement, on the same seats that customers with respectable clothes use! That'll be good for a laugh!" Slowly, the pubs ceased to be convivial places in which to spend a pleasant hour or two. They began to die.

Three other things brought about the end of the English pub. Once upon a time, country people earning £3 a week could afford two or three pints of beer a day. Most of them did! At todays prices of almost £2 a pint, this would mean £42 per week. In short, the ratio of drink prices to earnings, has not been in proportion. Very few people can now afford to pay the current prices.

The advent of convenience foods and microwave cooking, has resulted in the most inedible foods coming from the kitchens of most country inns. Customers now prefer eating in their own homes, rather than at the local hostelry. Probably even the managers cannot remember, when a typical meal at a public house consisted of a beautiful pork chop (complete with crackling) roasted in the oven, with apple sauce, roast potatoes, parsnips and Savoy cabbage, followed by *real* Spotted Dick and custard, all with real flavours and not a tasteless mass. It seems to me that anything labelled 'home made' is a 7 lb tin of steak and kidney, looking like a dark-brown, masticated mass, shot into an earthenware bowl, with a slab of frozen puff pastry slapped on the top. This, after five minutes in the microwave oven, is then placed on your plate (regardless of what it has been standing in) and accompanied with a pile of sad-looking mixed salad (this is cheap and looks a lot). Potato chips are then added that are nothing more than frozen reconstituted potato. Any broccoli has been frozen and comes straight out of a packet, any mushrooms are out of a tin and simply dunked in hot water. Everything tastes the same and costs the earth. Empty public houses and restaurants are testimony to these facts.

The final nail in the coffin, was the result of a natural progression of events. The country inn flourished when locals visited it on foot, bicycle, or bus. To be nine sheets to the wind on foot, was no great problem; you simply fell in the hedge. To be in the same state on a bicycle, resulted in a similar conclusion, although travelling a bit faster, you still fell in the hedge. If the condition was the same on a bus, the conductor looked after you as far as your bus stop. Your promptly fell in the hedge when you got off. All that happened was that you fell in the hedge and caused no one any harm.

The march of time – and progress brought the motor car. This brought about the demise of the bus. To be nine sheets to the wind in a motor car was a completely different kettle of fish. You do not fall in a hedge in a motor car – you either kill yourself, or the person that you hit! After many years of drunk drivers killing themselves and members of the public, the police introduced the breathaliser.

This, together with the falling standards of the public house, the excessive charges for a beverage that is ninety per cent water, the awful apology that is served in the name of food, has resulted in the character of the country pub being changed completely. They are now but shadows of what they used to be.

When one faces the prospect of suffering all these changes, and possibly finding all the wheels stolen from ones car in the pub car park, is it any wonder that folk choose to have a meal in their own home, a glass of wine by their own fireside and, after a pleasant evening viewing the television, to retire in a mellow state to the comfort of ones own bed. Memories of the good times are precious indeed!

CHAPTER TWENTY-NINE

A Golden Age

It is good to reminisce – to think of times past and to reflect on the age that we lived in. It is even better to sit back and smugly smile, at the mess that the present day whizz-kids have got us all in!

It was all to do with the crazy attitude of self-expression that seemed to be the fashion of the fifties and sixties.

We have lived in a golden age of achievements, where human endeavour exceeded all bounds.

Gordon Richards finally won the Derby – we never thought that he would.

Alcock and Brown flew the Atlantic and ended up on their noses in an Irish peat-bog.

We built the R101. What an achievement that was; 724 ft long, 132 ft in diameter, and filled with 5 million cubic feet of highly explosive gas. It had five massive 600 hp engines that made up a quarter of its total weight. With wrought ironwork, potted ferns and a grand piano, it was simply too heavy to fly. It was a wonder that it took the air. The truth of the matter was, that it did not. It staggered into the air on its initial flight, finally sagging to its demise in the fields of northern France. Many people died.

Roger Bannister broke the physiological barrier of the

first four minute mile; many others have since accomplished this feat.

Stanley Matthews won the cup final for Blackpool, he finally received a well-deserved knighthood.

England won the World Cup; the chances are that we will never do it again.

Edmund Hillary and Sherpa Tensing reached the summit of Mount Everest. Edmund Hillary was knighted. Many climbers have since repeated this feat.

John Hartle broke the lap record at the Isle of Man TT at over 100 mph on a Norton.

John Surtees became in the only world champion in both cars *and* motor cycles.

Things that we take for granted; radio, television, washing-machines, electric blankets, electric irons, microwave ovens, refrigerators, telephones, computers; were all invented.

Aeroplanes went so fast that they broke the sound barrier. Britain and France have built one that flies twice as fast. It is called *Concorde*. It takes passengers to America in just over two hours.

The Russians sent a dog into space. The Americans went to the Moon and walked on it.

Giant space rockets 300 ft high regularly fly into space, they are building huge satellites that are to be inhabited. This does not even warrant a mention in the newspapers.

Somebody decided to dig a tunnel under the Channel between England and France. It was done. We have ceased to be an island.

With the advent of the European Economic Community, we are now in the process of becoming part of a European super state.

People now throw themselves off high bridges into

bottomless chasms. They do this with giant elastic bands tied to their feet. They call it 'bungee' jumping. Evidently they bounce up and down until they have had enough. What an odd world it is that we live in!

I made no apologies for the fact that I am unashamedly square. I do not like exhibitionists, rudeness, the unclean, coarseness, or drugs. It was a strange, self-destructive attitude in the later years, that seemed to encourage these things.

Four young men with long hair also jumped up and down (not quite like the 'bungee' jumpers). For five minutes they screamed 'We all live in a yellow submarine'. They were much acclaimed and became famous. Their particular forté was that not only did they defy convention, but that they were rude with it; they spawned many similar groups who – all in the interests of defying convention – were coarse and unclean. They promoted the drug scene.

A television series was introduced called *That Was the Week That Was*. It ridiculed the monarchy, the church, and the establishment.

A similar series was introduced on television. It was called *Spitting Image*. It lampooned the personal characteristics of its victims. It was supposed to be clever. It was vulgar and destructive.

A singer with greasy locks and a sullen expression, did the splits on stage and sang songs that were unintelligible. His name was Elvis Presley. He became the greatest success of all. He was called 'The King!'

'Graffiti', the respectable name for writing obscenities on walls, is ignored by the police. They are only human – they look the other way rather than risk a punch on the nose by the perpetrators. When the full weight of the law prosecutes an old age pensioner for stealing a toilet roll, but ignores an alleged multi-million pound embezzlement from a pension fund – money destined for other pensioners – it would seem to indicate that law and order has broken down. So much for a golden age that started off so well, but ended up such a disaster. Apart from living in it, at least I had nothing to do with it!

The end of my time, however, has concluded on a good note. The completion of my first book *This Forgotten Place*, resulted in a kind invitation by Dan Sloan of the Chelsfield Village Society, to a book-signing to be held at Chelsfield Village Hall. It was a pleasant evening with an attendance four times the normal.

I stated in this first book that it would be the only story that I would write on the subject of life at the old cottage and the dear people who lived in it. I was wrong. Apart from the fact that it sold 980 copies in the first two weeks of publication and was sold out within the year, the seven boys who were mentioned in the book all made contact. Tales were recounted at that first meeting. These, when added to stories of past events heard at the Chelsfield Village Society meeting, were enough, in fact, to write another book.

So the idea for *And Then There Were None* was conceived. It was to widen the scope of the story to include the immediate area around the old cottage, and the hamlet of Maypole. Because of the success of the first book, 1200 copies of the new one were ordered by bookshops prior to the day of publication. It was completely sold out in three months. The manager of the largest chain of bookshops in the country said, that although it was of local interest, it stood on its own merits as a very good story.

An identical situation occurred with the launch of the new book. There was, however, one important difference. My friend, Bob Hogben, the last of 'The Maypole

Boys' still living in Chelsfield village, suggested that it would probably be the only chance left, to invite the remaining people of our time, to a last meeting at Chelsfield village hall.

CHAPTER THIRTY

A Meeting of Old Friends

It was decided to extend an invitation to all the people of our time, together with any others that might be interested from the village, to a meeting at the village hall.

An invitation was printed and circulated. It said *You are cordially invited to a unique occasion: A meeting of Old Friends From Chelsfield Village.* It invited all those from the past, to spend an afternoon together to talk about old times. A raffle was organised. All the profits would be divided between the Village Hall Committee and St Martin of Tours. Refreshments in the form of tea and cakes would be provided, and talks given by Ann Blatcher on Chelsfield Church, and Philip Lane (who also provided a remarkable display of antique photographs of the area) who spoke on old photography.

It truly was an afternoon to be remembered. So many people came back. So many came from so far. The first person that I saw was Bob's sister, Doris. She had come over from Canada. Her opening remark to me was "Do you remember that damn dog of your Grandad's? I think his name was Trimmer. My God! What a dance that dog led me!"

I asked her – with my tongue in my cheek – what she meant. She said, "Every time that I had occasion to pass your cottage, that awful dog would shoot out and attack me in a most embarrassing way! His passion got the better of him!"

I said that he had probably got fed up with Grannie and found her much more attractive. Doris said that she even spoke to her father about it. He said that he had a talk to Grandad, who showed him "Trimmer, walkin' about wiv a bleedin' white bow tied on 'is weddin' gear." He felt by this that something had already been done about it. The truth of the matter was, that Bill Hogben knew that Grandad was pulling the wool over his eyes. He had heard from George Humble about the episode with the bandage from Neal's Stores. It was just that Bill Hogben could feel for Trimmer. He was having similar problems with his own dog, a brown and white spaniel named *Jerry*, and was being continually threatened by his wife, that either he had the dog doctored, or she would do it herself!

Both he and Grandad kept a sharp look out for the warning signs on their respective dogs, and contrived to get them out of the way when passion reared its ugly head.

Alec Stevens arrived with his son and daughter-in-law. He provided much information on old Mr Uhlrich and confirmed a picture of the old mans house that had been in some doubt. It transpired that at sometime in the past the picture had been imposed the wrong way round, with the result that the present picture is a mirror image of what the old place had actually been like.

Alec also distanced himself from any association with Trimmer. He said that the dog had originally been the property of Bryan's father who had dumped him on Grandad when Bryan had arrived on the scene. It would seem that Dorrie had the same problems as the rest of the women in the household. Dorrie had told Alf Yates that either the dog went or she would. Grandad considered the attitude of all the women involved completely unreasonable. Trimmer ultimately died of old age. He is buried to the right of the top garden gate, near to the holly tree.

To the left of the garden gate, was the place where any pets that died were buried. This would be any kittens, rabbits, mice, baby birds, the odd chick, a tortoise, and several goldfish. To the best of my knowledge there were also many matchboxes buried containing newts, tadpoles, and the odd worm or two. Every corpse that was buried in the 'pets graveyard' was neatly packed in its own coffin; it was wrapped in cotton wool and laid out with great religious fervour. The individual graves were usually marked out with pebbles. A cross of some sort would indicate the name of the occupant.

A burial service, hands together and kneeling in prayer, would always accompany any interment. This would be conducted with great sincerity and depth of feeling.

Sadly, this sincere depth of feeling never lasted. Boys will be boys. These graves would never remain intact for long – curiosity would always get the better of us. Bryan and I would dig them up after a week or two, to see what they smelled like, and how they looked in their various stages of decomposure.

Joan, the wife of Albert Stevens came back. She has married again and is now Joan Smith. Joan obviously relates to the years associated with Grannie and Grandad, and has memories of happy times spent at the old cottage. Joan is now over 75 years of age. She is still as attractive as she always was. My cousin Margaret came up from Brixham in Devon. Margaret is like a good wine, she improves with age. With every year that I get older, she seems to get younger. It is a pity that she lives so far away.

Probably for the last time, we four kids were all together. Bryan, Margaret, Dennis and myself. We all have aches and pains now, things are beginning to fall apart. It was the same with everyone else. Most seemed to need spectacles, baldness seemed to be encroaching fast, thank goodness there was no evidence of deaf aids. The most noticeable concession to age, apart from greyness, was a certain thickening of the midriff. Most people could now be described as portly.

Charlie Wickenden came down from the home counties, Colin Mortimer arrived from Westerham. Kathleen (Bob's sister) came from Romford with her husband. She was a sweet girl who we were all in love with at some time or another. She is still just as kind as she always was.

There were one or two problems. Namely that memories fade with the years. It was some time before old friends recognised each other. I noticed Bryan smiling benignly at a dear little woman with thick spectacles. "I'm afraid I don't know who you are," he was saying apologetically. Reg Mitchell was signalling frantically behind her back that it was his old childhood sweetheart, Mary Blott. I spoke at some length with Charlie Wickenden. I noticed the expression on his face when he realised who it was that he was talking to – it was fifteen minutes after we had begun our conversation. Joan Stevens had a tear in her eye; meeting Alec, her first husbands brother, doubtless brought back memories of earlier times.

The village hall was packed. They came from everywhere. It was uncanny, it was for all the world as if people continued conversations that they had been having fifty years ago. It was as if we were one large family, as if there was a common bond that bound us all together.

It was at this meeting that several things became apparent. I had never realised, that because Grandads brother George had a daughter, Elsie, who had married Bert Wickenden, that all her children were in fact second cousins to Bryan and me. At a stroke, we had eight relatives that we never knew we had before – they were all there! I also realised, that although everyone from the village and the surrounding area had been invited, only five of the local community made the effort to come. Four of them did, because they were genuinely interested in the village and our time, and Dan Sloan, because I knew that he would. Dan has a manner that is compatible with the people of our time. When Dennis Packham asked that a prize that he had won should be put up for auction, it was Dan Sloan who made the highest offer. Dan seemed genuinely amazed at the proceedings; he kept repeating "I can't believe it, I just can't believe it!" I think he was astounded that so many people had returned to the place of their childhood, that it was for all the world as if there had never been a fifty year gap.

It was this lack of interest by the local people that made me realise with crushing reality that our time had passed. I bear these people no malice, times are different, values are different, they are different. I have a great sadness, that because life is the way it is, their lives are insular. They have not lived the life that we did and are poorer because of it.

Three hours passed in a whisp of time. All too soon farewells were being said. Regrets were expressed at the questions that were meant to be asked but forgotten. There were so many friends from the past, so many enquiries to be made, but now it was too late, they were all gone. It was all over. Like us, it had passed into the oblivion of time.

I met Bob a few days later. He had a feeling of dejection about him. We spoke of the events of that day. He suggested that it might be possible to organise another meeting at a future date. I said it had been a unique occasion, there would never be another meeting like it. Sadly he agreed.

CHAPTER THIRTY-ONE

The Time Capsule

The seven Maypole boys mentioned in *And Then There Were None* (the second book of the trilogy), having been brought together by the first book, *This Forgotten Place*, now meet from time to time. There is no regularity to these occasions. They are held when we feel that the time is right – too often might spoil things. Generally, it would seem that they take place about every three months.

There is no formality when we meet, there is no committee and no agenda. It is simply a meeting of like-minded people. The only principle that governs ones eligibility to attend, is that they should have a genuine interest in the events of our time.

We meet at any one of the four public houses that mark the perimeters of the area in which we lived; the *Five Bells*, the *Bo-Peep*, the *Rock and Fountain* and the *Kent Hounds*. They are not particularly alcoholic occasions. We have a meal that is good value for money, and is as near as possible to the food of our time. The food, however, is incidental – it is simply an excuse for a meeting, it is the company that is important. All we do is meet old friends and talk of past times.

As almost all that meet on these occasions spent part of their lives at the village school, it was decided to approach the head-teacher, Mrs Brenda Norman, to see if it would be possible (prior to the next meeting at the *Five Bells*), for us to have a look at the place where most of us spent our formative years. Mrs Norman readily agreed, our request was opportune. It coincided with a day in which the pupils were engaged on a scheme that took them to other parts. We had the school to ourselves.

This visit was memorable. The main structure of the building was still as it always had been, but all the rooms seemed smaller. This was certainly an optical illusion. There were now ten of us who were all nearly six feet tall with an average weight of 14 stone, we seemed to fill the school.

Someone pointed out an odd marking on the floor. They said that it was where an old pot-bellied stove used to stand: it had a large fireguard with a brass rail on the top. This was where kids would hang wet gloves, socks, and scarves to dry, after their owners had either fallen in one of the three ponds in the area, or got soaked throwing snowballs on their way to school. The stench given off by the wet wool was awful

Comments were made about the exact place that the 'Nit Nurse' had stood, when she made her selection as to whether she sent you to the left or the right. You prayed that you would be sent to the left. This meant that you could return to your class; you sat smugly whilst some of your contemporaries were sent to the right and disgrace. You could not wait to get home to tell Grannie, who amongst the neighbours had got 'Nits'.

When we were looking around the playground, many were the comments made about who did what, with whom and where. Knowing looks passed between friends, and many an eye had a twinkle, at what really did happen behind the bicycle sheds.

It was generally agreed that there had been a feeling of comfort and warmth about Chelsfield Village School. It was a sad day when the time came to go on to other schools. Most of us initially went to Orpington Central School at Charterhouse Road: it is a shock to find a housing estate where this once stood not so long ago. One wonders where the thousands of children went, who attended this fine establishment?

Memories were expressed on the magical times had at Christmas, the excitement of the Christmas play. The marks were still there, although barely visible, where festoons of hand-made paper chains were regularly fixed each year, with drawing pins to plaster-board ceilings.

The worn steps told a story of countless thousands of tiny feet, either staggering in (as Bryan's had done, in a state of collapse when Eric Sampson had rung the bell early) or rushing out, to join in the merriment of sliding on the pond in the winter, or scrumping strawberries on the way home in summer.

Two of the items laid out for us to look at were the actual registers of all who had attended the village school going back to 1895. These were, in fact, a complete history of our time. They covered the years from 1885 to 1946. It was uncanny, almost like peeling the skins from an onion, to go back through the ages. To the last of our grandparents, the dates of admission of our parents, and the beginnings of our own times. They were all there.

From my own family there were Dorrie, Wilfred, and a sad entry of a little girl, aged four; that of my own mother, Nelly Packham. John Blundell was there, together with his sister, Joan. So too were the Stevens boys, Sid, Albert, and Alec. Bryan completed the picture.

It would seem that twenty-five of the pupils listed, were all related to my family.

I have borrowed these registers. They are in need of refurbishment. I would like to include a summary of their contents because they will be of interest – not only to the descendants of the pupils listed, but to historians of country life. They are precious indeed and contain information that should be preserved for all time.

A study of these registers firstly reveals that pupils attended Chelsfield Village School in 1885. It would seem that the actual registers were either dated incorrectly as 1895, or entries were back-dated to the original admission dates ten years earlier.

There are several other interesting observations. The 1838 County Archives map of Chelsfield and Maypole would seem to show more dwelling houses in the Maypole and Well Hill areas, rather than in the village of Chelsfield. This can be verified by the fact that initially very few of the pupils at the village school actually came from the village.

Another interesting fact is that these were feudal times. Most of the dwelling houses in the surrounding hamlets were tied properties, lived in by the land workers of the landed gentry. There was no such thing as birth control. Large families were the norm. It will be noted that there were many names that came from the same row of cottages, indeed as many as six or seven from individual cottages.

There was no dividing line to be drawn between the poor. Those who lived in the Maypole cottages adjoining Albert Blott's house, and those who lived in the tumble-down cottages on Back Hill, considered that their brick-built houses made them socially superior to those who inhabited the corrugated-iron shacks that constituted

Miller's Huts. The occupants of these huts, in turn, lorded it over the caravan dwellers that occupied the same site. Because these caravan dwellers occupied a site that had semi-permanent shacks, they considered that they were a cut above the caravans sited on Well Hill. The truth of the matter was, that they were not. They were all very poor, they all smelled of wood fires. They all lived, and looked like, gypsies.

Grannie Packham was one of sixteen children from the Keepers' Cottage in Shoreham Woods. There are several examples in these registers of other large families of children that occupied similar cottages:

> Nine members of the Smith family occupied the cottage known as Rounds.
>
> Six occupied the cottages at Bucks Cross
>
> Ten came from Hollybush Lane
>
> Seven came from *Yewtree House*
>
> Eight came from Miller's Huts
>
> Seven came from various caravans
>
> Fifty-two children attended the village school from the hamlet of Maypole
>
> Seventy children attended the village school from the hamlet of Well Hill

Several changes are noted:

With the spread of housing estates in 1927, new entries are noted from the Craven Estate. Sixteen children were admitted from these sources.

The erection of the council houses at Kilnfields, resulted in a new influx of children. Eighteen were admitted from these sources.

Biblical names were the noted preference of the poorer classes. A glance through these registers could reveal details of past origins. Common names listed are:

Abraham, Shadrach, Daniel, Septimus, Eliza, Thurza, Edwin, Patience, Adelaide, Rosa, Mabel, Queenie, Annie, Myrtle, Ruby, Blanche, Fanny, Dolly, Edmund, Bertha, Samson, Selena, Elijah.

The following pages are abstracted from the Admission Register of 1895.

Chelsfield Primary School

Admission Register 6th May 1895

Admission	Name	Address
5.8.1885	Frank Foreman	Well Hill, Shoreham
4.6.86	James Smith	'Rounds', Chelsfield
12.6.86	Richard Smith	'Rounds', Chelsfield
22.6.86	Gertrude Dunmall	Hollybush Lane
16.8.86	Winnie Cork	Well Hill, Chelsfield
4.10.86	John French	Well Hill, Chelsfield
5.10.86	Fred Foreman	Holly Bush Lane
11.10.86	Jesse Latter	Well Hill, Chelsfield
18.10.86	Florence Smith	Well Hill, Shoreham
10.3.87	Martin Daisy	Maypole, Chelsfield
28.3.87	Louisa Stone	Well Hill, Chelsfield
5.4.87	Arthur Smith	'Rounds', Chelsfield
26.9.87	William Blundell	Well Hill, Shoreham
3.10.87	William Salmon	Well Hill, Shoreham
9.4.88	Maurice Thomas	Well Hill, Shoreham
30.4.88	Mary Parrott	Skeet Hill, Orpington
14.5.88	Abraham Whitehead	May Pole
15.5.88	Elizabeth Whitehead	Well Hill, Shoreham
18.6.88	Emily Morgan	Well Hill, Chelsfield
5.7.88	David Morgan	Well Hill, Chelsfield
27.8.88	Arnold Winchcombe	May Pole, Chelsfield
8.10.88	Archibald Griffiths	May Pole, Chelsfield
11.3.89	Frank Stone	May Pole, Chelsfield
11.3.89	Edgar Gregory	Shoreham Lane
18.3.89	Hilda Cork	Well Hill, Chelsfield
20.5.89	Roland Smith	'Rounds', Chelsfield
30.12.89	Francis Swift	May Pole, Chelsfield
17.3.90	Emily Rose Whitehead	Yew Tree Corner
31.3.90	Archibald Dunmall	Holly Bush Lane, Chelsfield
28.4.90	Frederick Hills	Well Hill, Chelsfield

Admission	Name	Address
2.7.88	George Horton	Slutts Hole, Chelsfield
28.4.90	Arthur Horton	Slutts Hole, Chelsfield
19.5.90	Florence Salmon	Well Hill, Shoreham
29.9.90	Jesse Thomas	Well Hill, Shoreham
29.9.90	Henry Foreman	Well Hill, Shoreham
30.9.90	Maud Whitehead	Well Hill, Shoreham
3.11.90	George William Miles	May Pole, Chelsfield
9.3.91	Edwin Smith	Well Hill, Chelsfield
9.3.91	Thomas Morgan	May Pole, Chelsfield
6.4.91	John Thurlow	Skeet Hill, Orpington
6.4.91	Ethel Smith	Well Hill, Shoreham
20.4.91	Fredrick Gregory	Shoreham Lane
4.5.91	Lilian French	The Village, Chelsfield
19.5.91	Robert Stone	May Pole, Chelsfield
25.5.91	Albert John Miles	Well Hill, Shoreham
1.6.91	Albert Hicks	Bucks Cross, Chelsfield
1.6.91	Olive Hicks	Bucks Cross, Chelsfield
15.6.91	Amy Hicks	Bucks Cross, Chelsfield
12.10.91	Rose Hayes	May Pole, Chelsfield
30.11.91	Ada Lambert	Lone Barn, Orpington
25.1.92	William Whitehead	May Pole, Chelsfield
15.2.92	Maud Smith	'Rounds', Chelsfield
15.2.92	Kate Smith	'Rounds', Chelsfield
24.4.92	Harry Lambert	Lone Barn, Orpington
30.5.92	Thomas Smallwood	The Village, Chelsfield
7.6.92	Elizabeth Tanner	The Village, Chelsfield
7.6.92	Ellen Tanner	The Village, Chelsfield
22.8.92	Kate Blackwell	The Village, Chelsfield
4.10.92	Arthur Morgan	May Pole, Chelsfield
24.10.92	William Hathrill	Well Hill, Chelsfield
21.11.92	Arthur Whitehead	Yew Tree Cottages
14.3.93	Shadrach Whitehead	May Pole, Chelsfield
24.4.93	Ethel Marriott	The Village, Chelsfield
15.5.93	Alice Whitehead	The Firs, Chelsfield

Admission	Name	Address
11.9.93	Arthur French	The Village, Chelsfield
15.1.94	Daniel Whitehead	May Pole, Chelsfield
16.1.94	Thomas Wickenden	Packs Cottages, Chelsfield
29.1.94	Emily Palmer	Bo Peep, Chelsfield
19.3.94	Alfred Groom	The Village, Chelsfield
19.3.94	Horace Groom	The Village, Chelsfield
2.4.94	Edith Hayes	May Pole, Chelsfield
2.4.94	Rose Smith	Well Hill, Shoreham
9.4.94	Ada Winchcombe	Bo Peep, Chelsfield
30.4.94	Jane Devine	Well Hill, Shoreham
25.6.94	Frank Blundell	Well Hill, Shoreham
6.8.94	Arthur Augustus Tanner	The Village, Chelsfield
1.10.94	Ada Botting	'Rounds', Chelsfield
18.3.95	Emma Tanner	The Village, Chelsfield
24.4.95	Frederick Dunmall	Bo Peep, Chelsfield
8.5.94	Ernest Gardener	Packs Cottages, Chelsfield
17.10.95	Septimus Stone	May Pole, Chelsfield
2.3.96	Walter Winchcombe	May Pole, Chelsfield
2.3.96	Frederick Goldsmith	Bo Peep, Chelsfield
12.5.96	Eliza Hayes	May Pole, Chelsfield
16.11.96	Ernest G. Tichner	Well Hill, Shoreham
30.11.96	Agnes Collins	Well Hill, Shoreham
5.1.97	Richard Tanner	May Pole, Chelsfield
7.1.97	Richard Turner	'Rounds', Chelsfield
8.2.97	Thurza Tanner	May Pole, Chelsfield
12.2.97	Annie Tanner	May Pole, Chelsfield
29.3.97	Kathleen Devine	Well Hill, Shoreham
4.5.97	Dorothy Wickenden	Pecks Cottages, Chelsfield
4.10.97	Fanny Swift	Chelsfield
1.11.97	Emily Checksfield	Chelsfield
22.1.97	May Turner	Chelsfield
27.4.98	Lily Crowhurst	Well Hill, Shoreham
16.5.98	Frederick Checksfield	Bo Peep, Chelsfield

Admission	Name	Address
9.8.98	George Salmon	Well Hill, Shoreham
22.8.98	Jessie French	Chelsfield
7.11.98	John Tanner	May Pole, Chelsfield
6.12.98	Elsie Packham	Station Cottages, Shoreham
14.2.99	Edwin Whitehead	Yew Tree Cottages, Chelsfield
6.3.99	Lily Morgan	Maypole Cottages, Chelsfield
10.4.99	Rose Jarvis	Chelsfield
10.4.99	Sidney Checksfield	Chelsfield
15.5.99	Kenneth Stone	Well Hill, Chelsfield
15.5.99	Naphthali Chalk	Warren Road, Chelsfield
29.5.99	William Jarvis	Holly Lane, Chelsfield
9.10.99	Grace West	Pecks Cottages, Chelsfield
13.2.1900	Joseph Potter	May Pole Cottages, Chelsfield
8.3.00	Dora Tanner	May Pole, Chelsfield
23.4.00	Arthur Charman	Bo peep, Chelsfield
24.4.00	Fred Smith	Chelsfield
7.5.00	Kate Emily Whitehead	May Pole, Chelsfield
14.5.00	Alice Wickenden	Pecks Cottages, Chelsfield
1.10.00	Elsie Blackwell	Skibbs Lane, Chelsfield
6.5.01	Blanch Arnott	Yew Tree Corner, Chelsfield
30.1.01	Bertie Edwards	Millers huts
2.12.01	Patience Dighton	Millers Farm Caravans
2.12.01	Walter Dighton	Millers Farm Caravans
10.12.01	Bessie Morgan	Tripes Farm
11.12.02	Fred Wickenden	Slutts Hole
12,5,02	William King	Millers huts
19.8.02	Fred Cook	Park Gate
19.8.02	Sidney Mitchell	The Firs. Well Hill. Chelsfield
9,2,03	Ernest Charman	Bo peep. Chelsfield
20.4 03	Adelaide Tanner	May Pole. Chelsfield
4.5.03	Willie Collins	Holly Lane, Chelsfield
16.6.03	Brewer Clark	Millers huts
22.6.03	Fred Mitchell	The Firs. Well Hill. Chelsfield
2.7.03	Edward Stone	Well Hill, Chelsfield

Admission	Name	Address
4.8.03	Rosa French	The Village, Chelsfield
11.8.03	Ada Bicknell	Well Hill, Chelsfield
21.3.04	Stanley Charman	Bo peep, Chelsfield
11.5.04	William Tickner	Millers huts
24.1.05	Hilda Collins	Holly Lane
7.3.05	Fred Crowhurst	Well Hill, Chelsfield
27.3.05	Doris Packham	The Village, Chelsfield
6.2.05	Dorothy Packham	The Village, Chelsfield
9,8,05	Hubert Blackwell	Skibbs Lane, Chelsfield
9.8.05	Wilfred Tho's Packham	YewTree Cottage, Chelsfield
12.2.06	Ethel Martin	The Village, Chelsfield
1.5.06	Harry Nelson Smith	Park Gate
9.8.06	Elizabeth Gregory	Hollybush Lane, Chelsfield
9.8.06	Amy Ethel Gregory	Hollybush Lane, Chelsfield
5.11.06	Nora Emily Hopkinson	1 Yewtree Cottage, Chelsfield
22.3.07	Gladys Smith	Cross Hall Cottage.Chelsfield
19.6.07	Arthur Checksfield	Hewitt Cottage, Chelsfield
7.10.07	Arthur Mitchell	Well Hill, Chelsfield
21.10.07	Ethel Tanner	Maypole Cottages, Chelsfield
15.6.08	Wm Ernest Malyan	Bungalow.Cray Lane
28.10.08	Ronald Checksfield	Hewitts Farm, Cheldfield
19.4.09	Harold Bowen	Halstead Station
26.4.09	George Arthur French	Goddington
16.8.09	Louis Alfred Foreman	Yew Tree Cottage, Chelsfield
23.8.09	Mabe Caroline Wright	Well Hill, Chelsfield
30.8.09	Fred Ernest Costin	Pecks Cottages, Chelsfield
16.8.09	Bessie Francis Morgan	Codlin Cottages.Chelsfield
27.9.09	James Whitehead	Maypole.Yew Tree.Chelsfield
7.3.10	Gladys Foreman	Well Hill, Chelsfield
22.8.10	William Blott	Well Hill, Chelsfield
17.10.10	Harold Denton	Black Cottages, Well Hill
28.11.10	Henry Cotteril	Black Cottages, Well Hill
27.2.11	Sydney Foreman	Skeet Hill
7.3.11	Lily Costin	Pecks Cottages.Chelsfield

Admission	Name	Address
20.3.11	Freda Tanner	Maypole.Chelsfield
4.4.11	Leslie Whitehead	Maypole, Chelsfield
4.4.11	Colin Turner	Worlds End Lane.Chelsfield
4.4.11	Archibald Sid'y Charman	White Hart.Chelsfield
1.5.11	Nellie Gregory	Yew Tree Corner
1.5.11	Queenie Dighton	Millers Farm huts
15.5.11	Montague Mitchell	The Firs, Well Hill
26.2.12	Annie Morgan	Maypole, Chelsfield
18.9.11	Alice Ada Mills	The Five Bells, Chelsfield
23.10.11	John Devine	Bucks Cross
27.2.12	Doris Morgan	Maypole
25.3,12	Nellie Packham	Yewtree Cottage
15.4.12	Lilly Gregory	Holly Lane, Chelsfield
20.5.12	Edmund Margetts	The Village, Chelsfield
30.9.12	Vera Burgess	Bucks Cross
28.10.12	Stanley Collins	Bucks Cross
9.10.12	Wm Arthur French	Well Hill, Chelsfield
10.2.13	Helena Divall	The Village
25.2.13	Ellen Costin	Maypole
29.4.13	Christopher Moxham	Well Hill
30.4.13	Matilda Moxham	Well Hill
16.6.13	Jane Bassett	Maypole Cottages
16.6.13	Christopher Bassett	Maypole Cottages
28.7.13	Violet Winchcombe	Well Hill
6.10.13	A.Checksfield	Hewitts Farm Cottages
27.10.13	Annie Cade	Craven Estate
4.5.14	Annie Bassett	Maypole
11.5.14	Wm George Alwen	Well Hill
6.10.14	Harold Smith	The Village
6.10.14	Osman Charles Margetts	The Village
12.4.15	Myrtle Crowhurst	Black Cottages
12.4.15	William Divall	The Village
12.4.15	Charlotte Parrott	Well Hill
17.5.15	May Whitehead	Maypole

Admission	Name	Address
25.10.15	Violet Smith	Cross Cottages
10.1.16	Stephen Bassett	Maypole
1.2.16	Reginald Butcher	School House
10.4.16	May Sparrowhawk	Church Road, Chelsfield
10.4.16	Charles Jarvis	c/o Mrs Martin, The Village
21.8.16	Violet Costin	Maypole Cottages
16.4.17	Elsie Alwen	Well Hill
27.8.17	Joan Blundell	c/o Mrs Packham, Maypole
15.10.17	Arthur Curtis	Well Hill
18.3.18	Horace Alexander Mills	Well Hill
8.4.18	Nora Foreman	Well Hill
15.4.18	Ruby Whitehead	Well Hill
16.4.18	John Blundell	Maypole
29.7.18	Charles Alfred Letch	Pecks Cottages
29.7.18	John Thomas	Well Hill
17.2.19	Blanch Collins	Well Hill
24.3.19	George Whitehead	Well Hill
29.4.19	Albert Styles	Lilys Farm
9.12.20	Fanny Dighton	Millers Farm
13.4.20	Herbert Parkes	Well Hill
5.10.20	Alec Stevens	Yewtree House
5.10.20	Sidney Stevens	Yewtree House
5.10.20	Albert Stevens	Yewtree House
28.7.20	Gladys Parkes	Well Hill
6.4.21	Colin Turner	Cross Cottages
15.5.23	William Sanderson	The Village
16.3.25	Irene Florence Hughes	Holly Lane, Chelsfield
28.4.25	Annie Challoner	Well Hill Cottages
8.6.25	Doris Tester	Lillies Farm, Chelsfield
8.6.25	Frank Tapsell	Craven Estate
10.6.25	Ernest Caleb Wm Still	Craven Estate
15.6.25	Rex Dunmall	Maple House
10.8.25	Herbert Ashby	Lillies Farm
11.8.25	Violet Sybil Smith	Court Lodge Farm

Admission	Name	Address
26.4.26	Nellie Read	c/o R. Foreman, Well Hill
27.9.26	Ivy Andrews	Holly Bush Cottages. Chelsfield
27.9.26	Percy Smith	Osbornes, Chelsfield
27.9.26	George Wickenden	Cross Hall Cottages
1.11.26	Doris Betty Hogben	6 Cross Hall Cottages
17.5.27	Dolly Collins	Caravan. Court Lodge Farm
27.6.27	Claude Toms	Lillys, Chelsfield
24.10.27	Charles Tapsell	Craven Estate, Cray Lane
29.3.26	George Austen Ashby	The Village, Chelsfield
23.11.27	Alfred Wm Marchant	Mount Hall, Chelsfield
9.1.28	Isabel Tanner	The Village, Chelsfield
12.3.28	William Bowers	Kiln Cottages, Chelsfield
12.3.28	Alice Bowers	Kiln Cottages, Chelsfield
12.3.28	Rose Bowers	Kiln Cottages, Chelsfield
20.3.28	Albert Weller	Kiln Cottages, Chelsfield
16.4.28	Roy Winchcombe	Well Hill, Chelsfield
16.4.28	Vera Wickenden	Cross Hall Cottages. Chelsfield
14.5.28	Patience Wickenden	Mount Hall, Chelsfield
26.11.28	James Leslie Walker	c/o Mrs Smith, Well Hill
7.1.29	Vera Thomas	Holly Lane, Chelsfield
7.1.29	William George Hogben	12 Kilnfield Houses, Chelsfield
25.2.29.	Ivy Weller	2 Council Houses, Kilnfield
5.6.29	Margaret King	Well Cottages, Well Hill
17.6.29	Rosemary Smallwood	The Village, Chelsfield
1.7.29	Alan Curtis	Kent Hounds, Well Hill
2.9.29	Kenneth Mitchell	The Firs, Chelsfield
2.9.29	Frederick Collins	5 Council Houses, Chelsfield
6.1.30	Ronald Smith	'Rounds', Chelsfield
20.1.20	George Tapsell	Craven Estate, Chelsfield Lane
28.4.30	Harold W. Wickenden	Saunders Cottage Shoreham Lane
1.9.30	John Henry R. Tanner	Bucks Cross
5.1.31	Roger Smallwood	Church Road, Chelsfield
5.1.31	Kathleen Hogben	Council Houses

Admission	Name	Address
5.1.31	Caroline Bowers	1 Council Cotts, Chelsfield
2.2.31	E.A.Checksfield	11 Kiln Field, Chelsfield
13.4.31	Charles Wickenden	Cross Hall Cottages
4.5.31	Eileen May Spooner	Parkgate Cotts, Chelsfield
14.9.31	Donald Wickenden	Shoreham Lane
14,9,31	Violet Sampson	Epsom Spring Cotts Warren Lane
4.4.32	Edmond Letchford	Well Hill, Chelsfield
4.4.32	Gertrude Letchford	Well Hill, Chelsfield
12.9.32	Gladys Marchant	Mount Hall, Maypole
23.1.33	Violet Webster	'Sunshine' Craven Estate
24.4.33	May Bowers	1 Council Houses, Chelsfield
16.10.33	Marjorie Wickenden	Cross Hall Cottages.Chelsfield
9.4.34	Charles Collins	5 Kiln Field Cotts, Chelsfield
9.4.34	Audrey Hickford	Mount Hall, Chelsfield
16.4.34	Vera Eileen Turner	Gladstone villa, Chelsfield
16.4.34	Alan Wickenden	Shoreham Lane, Chelsfield
17.9.34	Stanley Wickenden	Cross Hall Cotts, Chelsfield
17.9.34	Phyllis Alice Turner	Cross Hall Cottages.Chelsfield
17.9.34	Eileen Hogben	Council Houses.Chelsfield
31.10.34	Betty Blewett	12 Court Road.Orpington
17.6.35	Barbara Clapson	1 Black Cottages, Chelsfield
20.4.36	Betty Collins	8 Kilnfield Cotts.Chelsfield
20.4.36	Sylvia Blewett	Penwortham.Court rd.Orpington
20.4.36	Bertha Tanner	Bucks Cross, Chelsfield
8.6.36	Alfred Brooks	Well Hill, Chelsfield
8.6.36	Victor Alfred Webster	'Sunshine' Craven Estate
28.9.36	Eric Sampson	Craven Estate
5.10.36	Kenneth Stone	Well Hill
30.11.36	Bertie Sidney Bell	1 Maypole Cottages.Maypole
30.11.36	Thomas Wadey	1 Maypole Cottages.Maypole
11.1.37	Robert Hogben	12 Council Houses
30.11.36	Frank James Wadey	1 Maypole Cottages.Maypole
12.4.37	Reginald Mitchell	Bungalow.Woodlands.Chelsfield

Admission	Name	Address
12.4.37	Ronald Kemsley	2 Maypole Cottages. Maypole
19.4.37	John Clapson	1 Black Cotts, Well Hill
26.4.37	Mary Blott	Maple House, Chelsfield
3.5.37	Bryan Yates	Yewtree House, Chelsfield
5.7.37	Robert Hogben	12 Council Houses
13.9.37	Denis Mortimer	Merton, Chelsfield Lane
13.9.37	Colin Mortimer	Merton, Chelsfield Lane
13.9.37	John Preston	Westholme. Chelsfield Lane
13.9.37	Barbara Jewell	Ivy Cottage. Craven Estate
30.11.37	Donald Wedger	11 Kilnfield Council Houses
10.1.38	George Costin	Pillar Box, Well Hill
9.2.38	Brian Henry Curtis	Rock Cottages, Well Hill
25.4.38	Raymond Wadey	1 Maypole Cotts
25.4.38	John Costin	9 Kilnfields Cotts
12.9.38	Ronald Genders	314 Court Road
1.11.38	Donald Widger	11 Council Houses
14.11.38	Margaret Gidden	Victern, Chelsfield Lane
9.1.39	Ronald Marchant	Mount Hall
10.1.39	Rosina Salmon	Westwood Farm
23.1.39	Timothy Alwen	Sandown, Well Hill
5.6.39	Alan Tanner	Rose Cottage, Bucks Cross
19.9.39	Jean Bull	Lilys Farm, Chelsfield
2.10.39	Jeanette Parrott	The Poplars, Well Hill
9.10.39	Leonard Pritchard	Darenta, Well Hill
29.1.40	Derek Sparrowhawk	Court Lodge Cottage, Church Road
1.4.40	Colin Turner	5 Cross Hall Cottages
8.4.40	Eric Marr	4 Yewtree Cottage
18.4.40	Charles Letchford	Caravan, Well Hill
17.6.40	Sampson Smith	Hylands, Well Hill
22.7.40	Selena Letchford	Caravan, Well Hill
23.7.40	Dorcas Letchford	Caravan, Well Hill
21.10.40	Beryl Stoneham	Berwick, Chelsfield Lane
14.1.41	Ronald Ferrin	4 Black Cottages. Well Hill

Admission	Name	Address
28.1.41	Ronald Genders	386 Court Road
20.5.41	Beryl Scott	Holly Cottage, Chelsfield Lane
22.5.41	Shirley Skinner	Maypole Cottage, Maypole
9.6.41	Roy Widger	11 Council Houses
15.9.41	Clare Sanderson	Bransford, Craven estate
15.9.41	Valerie Skinner	Maypole Cottage, Maypole
6.10.41	Kenneth Buck	Bo Peep Cotts
15.10.41	Maurice Christmas	Annex, Goddington House
13.4.42	Anne Hillier	Maypole Cottage, Maypole
4.5.42	Gordon Purves	Sundown, Well Hill
18.5.42	Una Saunders	The Cottage, Skibbs Lane
31.8.42	Anne Saunders	8 Holly Lane
2.11.42	Ella Watson	Bucks Cross Farm
2.11.42	Agnes Watson	Bucks Cross Farm
4.11.42	Roger Freeman	Bo-Peep Cott
28.6.43	Peter Bowles	Maypole Cott, Maypole
6.9.43	Georgina King	Julian Brimstone Cott
18.10.43	Henry Caple	Whiteheads, Rock Hill
9.1.43	Colin Motton	Cross Hall Cottage
16.11.43	David Housago	Well Hill, Chelsfield
22.11.43	Elijah King	Whiteheads, Rock Hill
18.9.44	Roger Hillier	Maypole Cottage, Maypole
2.7.45	Phyllis Sanderson	Court Lodge Farm

EPILOGUE

When I began writing my first book, *This Forgotten Place*, it was my intention to share the humourous experiences that I had of the magical times of my youth in the old house in which I lived at that time. It was written as an epitaph to Grannie and Grandad Packham – the wonderful couple who started it all, and Grandad's brother, Ern.

The publication of *This Forgotten Place* resulted in the 'Maypole' boys – seven lads who went around together fifty years ago – meeting up again. Stories were recounted and memories revived. The result was another book. I gave it the title *And Then There Were None*. It was a broader chronicle of events that happened in the immediate area of the old house. This book concerned the daughters of the old people and their two unruly children.

I stated on the completion of *And Then There Were None*, that it was the end of a story. How wrong I was. Grannie once said to Grandad, when all their flock had flown, that it was the beginning of the end. Grandad replied, as they all returned one Christmas Eve, that it was more like the end of the beginning. That's how it was with this book.

The last of the 'Maypole' boys still living in Chelsfield, booked the village hall and issued invitations to: *A Last Meeting of the Old Friends of Chelsfield and*

Maypole. The hall was packed. They all came back. It was a unique occasion the like of this will never be seen again.

Since this event, the original seven 'Maypole' boys have increased in number. There are now eighteen of us. Our three-monthly meetings have become hilarious. It is because of the various anecdotes that I have heard, that I have been able to complete the trilogy. Some I would not dare to repeat. Others, have confirmed my belief that all the families of my time, had similar lavatorial experiences to the ones that we had. A cousin of mine, speaking of the difficulties of trying to do his homework in a kitchen full of screaming kids, asked his mother if he could conduct his studies in the sitting room. This was the best room in the house and reserved for special occasions only. Having her blessings to this request, he spread his school books and homework over the highly-polished table, and by the exceedingly dim light of an old-fashioned oil lamp, proceeded to try and see what the Theorem of Pythagoras was all about. He had shown some aptitude in the study of geometry; his teacher had lent him his own personal text books for research into the subject.

At some time during the proceedings, the paraffin oil in the lamp began to run out. Things began to smoke, floating particles of soot landed on his homework. His father was called to deal with the situation. Instead of taking the lamp to the kitchen to fill it with more paraffin, he tried to do this on the dining-room table. Having inserted the funnel, he decided that it was dangerous to perform this task with the lamp still alight. He extinguished the flame and tried to fill it in the dark. The inevitable happened – paraffin sloshed all over his sons soot-speckled homework. My cousin moaned at his mother and father about the trying conditions that he was having to work under, and also wailing about what excuse he was going to have to make to the teacher to account for his spoiled work, he was at least consoled by the fact that his teacher's personal text book was untouched . . . that was until a pipe burst in the room above.

A cascade of water suddenly poured through the ceiling. It landed smack in the middle of his teacher's text book, completely ruining it. My cousin, seeing his academic career in ruins, screamed for his mother to get Mr Divine, who had aspirations in the plumbing department, to come and mend the leak that was rapidly spoiling his homework as well as his reputation with the teacher.

Jack Divine insisted on finishing his supper. He finally arrived too late to save anything. The ceiling was ruined and needed another coat of whitewash. A man had to come in and french-polish the table top. My cousin had an awful job explaining away the disgusting state of his homework and the teachers ruined text book.

When asked to account for all his ruined books, he said weakly, that his sister had done it.

This was true in part. Luckily he was not asked to explain it further.

Jack Divine, after spending what seemed to be a lifetime with a bag of tools banging about in the room above, came down from upstairs as the vicar arrived on one of his monthly visits. My cousin's mother, suspecting the worst, did a good job of convincing him that it was a regular occurrence and only a burst water pipe in the room above. The vicar was most concerned that a leaking water pipe should have caused so much damage. He was almost at the point of asking the Lord to help them in their hour of need, when Jack Divine appeared.

He said in a most ungodly way, "That 'ent no burst pipe. Yer sister's jest kicked the piss-pot over agin!"

There were red faces all round. It seemed that the more my cousin's mother tried to explain it all away, the more embarrassing the situation became. Jack Divine made a coarse remark about "the vicar blessing the wrong holy water," and went happily on his way. It was nice to know that others had the same problems with chamber-pots that we did.

At each of our meetings I seem to meet more people of our time – new facts come to light. Ken Mitchell remarked how well he got on with old Jack Tanner, the special policeman who caused us so many dreadful problems, particularly with reference to Henry May's cherry orchard!

In response to a complaint from Mr May, it was Constable Tanner who was delegated by Sergeant Carver to catch whoever it was that was stealing vast quantities of produce, from various parts of the complainant's farm.

Constable Tanner did a good job. He hid in the orchard and hotly pursued four lads who he caught scrumping cherries. He never actually caught any of them, but he recognised who they were. By telling all their mothers that all the rest had confessed to the crime, he obtained confessions from all of them. It was a police court job which resulted in the case being thrown out as too trivial.

It was Ken Mitchell who said that he met Constable Tanner coming home one evening after a long vigil in the orchard. The saddle bag on his bicycle was bursting at the seams. "You've got a bit of a load on there, Jack!" said Ken with a twinkle in his eye. Looking at the juice running out from the seam of the saddle bag he said, "That looks for all the world like cherry juice!"

Constable Tanner replied, "Well, I don't see why them little buggers should git all the best pickings!" and went sheepishly on his way.

The truth of the matter was, that Henry May need not have looked very far for his missing produce. While Sergeant Carver was 'borrowing' his cauliflowers as quickly as Stanley could grow them, Jack Tanner was doing a crafty job looking after his cherries. Some things in this world never change!

It was a chance observation by Eric Sampson at the latest meeting of the Maypole Boys that brought another incident to mind. Talking of the winters of our time, Eric said, "My God, they were cold, there were times that ice seemed to cover the roads for weeks on end, and the grass at the sides of the lanes seemed to be stiff with hoar-frost for the whole of the winter."

His chance remark instantly reminded me of just such a time. . . .

It was the winter of 1940. For some odd reason – probably because of the tall Elm trees that stood opposite to the cottage and the overhanging Yewtree on our side, it seemed to make the lane underneath these trees an exceedingly cold place.

Because of the water that ran down the side of the cottage from Grannie's overflowing bucket, and this bitterly cold patch, the ice at this point was thicker, and stayed longer, than anywhere else in the parish. It was this that caused Bryan and me to decide to make a slide, fifty feet long, down the lane on the side nearest to Mrs Lambert's bungalow.

Mrs Lambert occupied the property opposite. She had seen better times and had once lived in the *White House* on the top of Well Hill. She was a kindly soul with a problem in the wind department. Grandad, ever the

height of propriety, said that bearing in mind her problem, it was the best possible place for her to have lived.
There was, however, not a lot to choose between her and
Grannie. I suspect that Mrs Lambert was a winner by a
nose, but the point was purely academic.

Mrs Lambert kept herself to herself, only coming into
contact with us when we needed to use her telephone, or
she needed to use our air-raid shelter when the air raids
were particularly bad.

Our slide turned out to be excellent, and by early afternoon had developed a highly-polished glaze. This gave
some indication of the speed that could be attained, and
the amount of slip that had developed.

It was when we had been called in for one of Grannie's
Saturday-lunch specials (bacon, Charlie Strout's famous
sausages, tomatoes, and a mountain of crispy bubble and
squeak), that Grandad – who unknown to us had been
studying points, after tentatively rubbing his foot back
and forth on our highly-polished slide, decided – after a
furtive look to see that he was unobserved – to have a go
himself. His mistake was in not looking carefully
enough. His brother, Ern, who had been digging carrots
from the frozen ground at the top of the garden, had wandered down to the cottage, hoping for a cup of tea from
Grannie. He stood with his mouth agape, amazed as he
saw Grandad, coat-tails flying, moving at an incredible
rate with arms outstretched like an ice skater, down the
entire length of our slide. He was further amazed when
he saw him repeating his performance, only this time
balanced on one leg, with the other stretched out behind,
his arms spread, like the wings of a graceful swallow.

Grannie, too, had watched the performance from the
pantry window. She was not particularly surprised at his
prowess. Grandad had always said that his ability at slid-

ing on the river in Eynsford gave him the potential of being a world championship skater. As in all things she believed him; nevertheless, she thought, "Silly show-off, without doubt he'll come a cropper. It 'ent right fer a man of 63 ter be actin' thataways!" She was right, of course, but not in the way that she expected.

Grandad came in for lunch, flushed with the exhilaration of his exploit, he was itching to tell everyone about it, but kept quiet; it was just the sort of 'silly caper' that he would have had a go at us for doing.

In the meantime, Mrs Lambert had trouble making up her mind what seed potatoes to order from Neal's Stores. She had decided to seek the opinion of Grandad – as she always did on matters horticultural. With her spectacles on the end of her nose and looking like a portly Miss Marple, she headed in the direction of our cottage.

In the meantime, Sergeant Carver had supped several free pints at the back door of the *Rock and Fountain*, and with a warm glow inside, was pedalling – with a bit of a wobble on – towards our cottage. His normal route home would have taken him past the council houses. Knowing that he was having problems keeping things straight, he decided to avoid any trouble by taking a more devious route to Hollybush Lane, via Maypole Corner and Shoreham Lane.

Thus it was, that Mrs Lambert and Sergeant Carver happened to be on a converging course, on the same stretch of lane, outside *Yewtree House* at the same time.

This was all very fortunate. The long arm of the law was on the scene as Mrs Lambert stepped on to our slide.

Sergeant Carver said that the first thing he saw of Mrs Lambert, was seeing her suspended, apparently levitated, three feet above the ground. The truth of the matter was, that her feet shot from under her at such a rate, that the trusty sergeant, having great trouble in focusing, only registered her (apparently motionless), hanging in space. That was until Mr Newton's first law of gravity became apparent. Mrs Lambert dropped like a stone and hit the ground with a hell of a thump.

The trusty sergeant mentally cursed his luck. Trust the old dear to slip up when he was only two minutes from the safety of his own front door, just as he was ready for his lunch, too. But Sergeant Carver had not got where he had by evading issues.

"Stay where you are Mrs Lambert, help is at hand!" he shouted. He proceeded to sedately dismount by throwing his leg, in a most policeman-like fashion, over the saddle of his bicycle. The intention was good but the implementation flawed. He caught his boot in the saddle-bag and fell spectacularly in the hedge.

Extricating himself in an undignified scramble, he assumed his most official manner. Striding towards the prone Mrs Lambert, he proceeded to take out his pencil and notebook. "Stay where you are, Mrs Lambert," he said (this was quite academic – Mrs Lambert was not going anywhere). He promptly stepped on the slide and, feet going in all directions, fell heavily on her prostrate form.

Scrambling up, and noticing the cause of all the problems – the slide – Sergeant Carver looked for someone else to blame. Seeing Grandad's brother, Ern, standing in the orchard he shouted, "Who made this bloody slide 'ere?" Ernie, because he had only seen Grandad performing on it, said in all innocence "Will did!"

"Right!" said Carver, "I'll bloody-well sort 'im out!"

Leaving Mrs Lambert prostrate in the lane, and breathing fire and brimstone, he came round to the back door and shouted at Grandad, "William Packham, you're not obliged to say anythin', but wot ever yer does says, I'll take dahn and bloody-well use agin yer!"

Grandad, not used to Sergeant Carver calling him William Packham instead of a friendly 'Will', sensed something was wrong.

"Wot's up then, mate?" he asked.

"Don't you bloody 'mate' me!" said Carver, "I'm 'avin' yer fer obstructin' the highway, gross bodily 'arm. preventin' a police hofficer from goin' about 'is business, an' generally behavin' like an 'ooligan! How's that fer a bloody start!"

"Wot's 'ee on about?" said Grandad, looking at Grannie. But Grannie, always nervous in the presence of the long arm of the law, scuttled into the pantry and banged a few saucepans about.

"There's old mother Lambert a'layin' out there mortally injured," steamed the sergeant, "all 'cos you made a bloody silly slide outside 'er front gate, that's a criminal charge if ever there was one!"

"I'm a'feared you've made a mistake old mate," said Grandad. "I 'ent made no bloody slide."

"That's the next charge!" shouted Carver, "Perjury!"

"Ow do yer make that out, then?" said Grandad.

"I asked yer brother Ern who made it," said Carver, "and 'ee said you did!"

At that moment, Grandad's brother Ern came in. "Wot did yer tell 'im I made a bloody slide fer?" said a narked Grandad. "Christ! Wiv a brother like you, who needs enemies."

"'Cos I see'd yer a'slidin' on it," said Ernie.

"That don't mean I made it!" shouted Grandad.

"You might as well confess," said Carver. "He's my witness that yer woz on the slide, and cos yer denied it after yer'd bin cautioned, that makes it perjury too!"

Grannie could see that the situation was getting out of hand. "I see'd 'im on it too," she said. "But it must 'ave bin there afore 'ee went on it, 'ee couldn't 'ave slid on it if it weren't there!"

Confronted with such logic, Sergeant Carver stopped his shouting and said "Well, who *did* make the bloody slide then?"

Grannie had seen Bryan and me sliding back and forth outside in the lane; she had also seen the pair of us beat a hasty retreat at the sight of the trusty sergeant appearing around the side of the cottage.

"The ice allus lays thick there," she said. "It's so cold under them trees; bin like it as long as I kin remember, anyways wot's 'appenin' about Mrs Lambert?"

In the heat of the moment, everyone had forgotten about the old dear from opposite, still laying in the lane outside.

"Christ!" said Grandad. "The poor old bugger will die of frostbite if we don't git a move on."

A procession of simple souls wended its way down to the lane outside, to see what could be done.

Mrs Lambert was in obvious pain, any attempt to move her, resulted in a yelp or two from one end, and a trump of protest from the other. It was decided to telephone Doctor Grant in Orpington for assistance.

There was a problem or two with the telephone. Apart from the fact that only Mrs Lambert knew how to work it, everyone else treated it with apprehension. Grandad stood with it held at arms length, and shouted from a distance; he then complained that he could not hear who he was talking to. Grannie did a shade better – she actually got the doctor. Her problem came when he asked her where the incident was. She seemed incapable of describing where Mrs Lambert lived. In reply to his question she said "In the lane outside," and nothing more. The fact that she had not said who she was, made things a shade difficult for Doctor Grant, but he was a country doctor and used to such things. He arrived in half an hour.

When Sergeant Carver was asked why he had not used the telephone instead of Grannie or Grandad, he said he "didn't know one end of it from the other."

After a consultation around the prone Mrs Lambert, the doctor diagnosed a broken leg. He said that she must be carried into her bungalow and kept warm until he arranged for an ambulance to take her to hospital.

Sergeant Carver had said no more about charging Grandad with obstruction, gross bodily harm, preventing a police officer from carrying out his duty, hooliganism, and perjury. Grandad had hoped that he had forgotten about it; events were to prove that the sergeant had other things to think about.

A conference was held, to decide how Mrs Lambert was to be carried back to the warmth of her kitchen to await the arrival of the ambulance. Grandad said this could be done by him and Ernie. Why did the sergeant not go home to the warmth of his own fireside, suggested Grandad (in view of the pending charges, anxious to curry favour) they could cope quite easily on their own. Sergeant Carver, not wishing to breathe too near the doctor, readily agreed and pedalled carefully on his way. Grandad got the short ladder from the ladder shed, and with help from Grannie and Ernie, gently loaded Mrs Lambert aboard.

The bumping of the ladder seemed to cause the old girl to play a merry tune. This caused some dissent from brother Ern. Grandad (forever crafty), had put him at the end where the fireworks were. "Why does it allus 'ave ter be me that comes along behind!" Moaned Ernie. "'Cos you're bloody deaf and can't hear a thing," said Grandad testily, adding; "And wot's more you're bloody-well cut out for it!" Ern mumbled and grumbled at the injustices of life, but through it all, he still managed to keep his end up!

The ambulance duly arrived, and Grannie, anxious to assist Mrs Lambert in every way, gathered several things together that she would need for her brief stay in hospital. It was when she was handing these over to the ambulance attendant, that she asked whether she should include one slipper or two.

"None I should think," said the ambulance attendant.

"Why ever not?" said Grannie. "She can't come 'ome in 'er stockin' feet!"

"She 'ent comin' 'ome fer a month or two," said the ambulance attendant.

"It don't take two months ter mend a broken leg," said Grannie.

"It does when there's two of 'em!" said the ambulance attendant.

"What's that supposed ter mean?" said Grannie.

"It means that she broke one when she fell over, and the police sergeant broke the other when he fell on it, said the attendant.

When Grannie returned to the cottage she broke the news to Grandad. To say that he was indignant would be an understatement. "Jest let 'im take me to court!" he said. "I'll tell 'em a thing or two, jest 'cos 'ee fell arse-over-tip on old mother Lambert an' broke 'er other leg, 'ent no cause ter be takin' it out on me!"

The next time Grandad met Sergeant Carver in the

lane, he said cockily 'ent heard nuffin from the court yet Sergeant?"

The Sergeant said "don't worry, you will do!"

Grandad said "'Ent you got another charge ter add ter the list then?"

"Wot's that then?" said the sergeant.

"Failin' ter report an accident involvin' personal injury," said Grandad.

Sergeant Carver gulped, and sheepishly dropped all charges. From that moment on, he and Grandad Packham seemed to have reached a happy understanding.

The release of *And Then There Were None* was an instant success. It sold out within four months of release. I know the last of the trilogy will be just as successful. The print run has been doubled, and reprints of the first two books have been placed. All these are due to be released at the same time.

My life has changed considerably since becoming involved in writing these stories. Some of the change has been good. My worry was that when my mother (who was not only my best friend but my greatest confidant) passed away, that my only connection with the old life would have gone forever. That connection was very important to me; when the tie linking the happiest times of ones life has been broken, it is as if an entire lifetime has suddenly gone. It is a feeling of desolation.

The whole world, however, seems to have turned full circle. These three books seem to have resurrected the old way of life. Every day I receive letters and telephone calls, either thanking me for bringing back thoughts of such wonderful times, or for the privilege of sharing the memories of my childhood with Grannie and Grandad in the old cottage. I have received countless letters from

Blundells all over the country – even from as far afield as Australia. And many from Packhams (Grandad's side of the family), mostly dispersed throughout Kent.

I do not profess to be a public speaker, but I have been invited in this capacity, as an after-dinner speaker, on several occasions. Whether I shall ever be asked back again or not, I do not know. The impression that I have is that audiences seemed to enjoy the tales of Grannie and Grandad and the old times.

At the launch of *And Then There Were None* I was invited to a book signing at W. H. Smith & Co Ltd in Orpington. While this was undoubtedly successful, the occasion was one of sadness. I parked my car in Spur Road and walked down the High Street. Wherever did Sherry's Restaurant go? What became of the *Commodore* Cinema? Where was Dr Grant's house? Where had all the old shops gone? Charlos, Stanley Woods, Edgars, Gilberts, Pipes, Cryers, Showells, Jays, Kings, the United Dairies, Meakers, Wiles, Caveys, Cave Austins, Patello Higgs? There were only two of the original premises left, the Post Office and Woolworths. Further down, at Orpington Pond, the *Palace* Cinema had gone, all the shops have changed. The *Blue Lagoon* swimming pool, together with a licensed premises, the *Bridge House*, are no more. Orpington, like the Chelsfield I knew, has gone.

This trilogy has been the story of Grannie, Grandad, their family, and their time. It was written to commemorate them, and their way of life. It has achieved that. Ten thousand people now know their story that did not know it before. I hope that they will be remembered for ever.

The end of this story came to me while looking through all the old birthday cards that my mother had kept over the years. She never enjoyed this day unless

she had a good cry. I would always write something sad
with this in mind. My last card to her seemed to contain
a message that very aptly concludes the end of this story
– it took the form of a poem:

One day we'll sail the depths of space,
and waken in another place,
There we'll quietly stand and wait,
for each other at the garden gate.
Hand in hand we'll wander through,
the old back door, to dear ones who,
have waited long, for us at last,
to join them from the old times past.
Dorrie, Bryan, you and me,
With Gran and Grandad making tea.
"Where 'ave yer bin?" Gran will say,
"We thought you'd gorn an' lost yer way,
"It's bin so long, we've missed yer so,
"The reaper's got no more ter mow.
"I know too, that you'd like to learn,
"We're damn-well stuck wiv brother Ern."
And that is how it all will end,
No more troubled paths to wend.
All round the fire, feeling fine,
Together till the end of time.

THE END

Derek Sheffield: Rolvenden, 1995